SENSATIONAL 90s QUIZ BOOK

SENSATIONAL 90s QUIZ BOOK

BRIAN WILLIAMS

First published in 2001 by
Miles Kelly Publishing Ltd
Bardfield Centre
Great Bardfield
Essex CM7 4SL

24681097531

ISBN 1 902947-48-7

Project Manager Ian Paulyn
Proofreader Lynda Watson
Cover Design Jo Brewer

E-mail info@mileskelly.net
Website www.mileskelly.net

INTRODUCTION

If you think you're suffering from short term memory lapses and the recent past seems to be receding into the grey mists of time the 90s Quiz Book is the equivalent to electric shock treatment on those lethargic frontal lobes. Think of the Spice Girls, Labour's landslide victory, Manchester United's last minute win in the European Cup and a feeling not unlike a rosy glow of nostalgia will rise in your breast. But hang on a minute wasn't the nineties the decade that brought us spin doctors, Chumbawamba and the Lewinsky Affair...

But whether you think the nineties were as over-inflated as the millennium dome or even as smooth and effortless as a David Beckham goal you can relive those heady days running up to the millennium as you romp through the quiz. And as those fond memories kick in – Liz Hurley wearing that dress, William Hague wearing his baseball hat and Michael Portillo wearing that expression – you can sit back and sigh and say, "Darling, it's all so last century!"

QUIZ 1

POT LUCK

1 Which musical instrument did Bill Clinton like to play?

2 What is the name of the Clintons' daughter?

3 What does DVD stand for?

4 What 90s phenomenon began in the 60s as ARPAnet?

5 Which Surrey player captained the England cricket team?

6 Which was John Prescot's favourite car?

7 Which British carmaker was unwanted by BMW as the 90s ended?

8 For which film did Gwyneth Paltrow win an Oscar?

9 Who wrote the original story *The Witches*, filmed in 1990?

10 Who starred as the Grand High Witch?

11 Which soccer club did Gerard Houllier manage?

12 And where did Derby County play home games in the 99-00 season?

13 For which TV channel did Peter Sissons work?

14 Did he a) read the news b) do impressions?

15 In which BBC TV comedy did Anette Crosbie star with Richard Wilson?

ANSWERS

1, Tenor saxophone 2, Chelsea 3, Digital Versatile (or Video) Disc 4, The Internet 5, Alec Stewart 6, Jaguar 7, Rover 8, *Shakespeare in Love* 9, Roald Dahl 10, Anjelica Houston 11, Liverpool 12, Pride Park 13, BBC 14, a) 15, *One Foot in The Grave*

QUIZ 2

PEOPLE

1 In what country was Silvio Berlusconi a media tycoon?

2 What job did George Carey take on in 1990?

3 Was he born in a) London b) Sydney c) Edinburgh?

4 Was Arsenio Hall a TV presenter or a baseball star?

5 Whose first names are Michael Ray Dibdin?

6 Who released a 1990 album called 'Back on the Block'?

7 Where was John Hewson a leading Liberal?

8 Whose role as the Engineer caused legal and theatrical trouble in the USA?

9 In which London show had he appeared?

10 And which US city at first said "no" to his appearing there?

11 Who made a 1990 album called 'Step by Step'?

12 In which US sport did Isiah Thomas excel?

13 Where was Hissen Habre overthrown in 1990?

14 Who led France's National Front?

15 What was the nationality of athlete Doina Melinte?

ANSWERS

1, Italy 2, Archbishop of Canterbury 3, London 4, A TV presenter 5, Heseltine 6, Quincy Jones 7, Australia 8, Jonathan Pryce 9, Miss Saigon 10, New York 11, New Kids On The Block 12, Basketball 13, Chad 14, Jean-Marie Le Pen 15, Romanian

QUIZ 3

ARTS & ENTERTAINMENT

1 In which film did Woody and Buzz Lightyear appear?

2 Which actor played Ace Ventura?

3 Who played the President in *The American President?*

4 What kind of animal was Babe?

5 What country did Asterix conquer in a 1995 movie?

6 Who played Jim Lovell in *Apollo 13?*

7 Which busty blonde played a girl called Barb Wire in a film of the same name?

8 Who was Batman in *Batman Forever?*

9 Who co-starred in that film as Harvey Two-Face?

10 Who played William Wallace on screen?

11 And the film?

12 Who was the male star of *The Bridges of Madison County?*

13 What was John Travolta's screen job in *Broken Arrow?*

14 Which actress played Dora Carrington in *Carrington?*

15 And which writer did Jonathan Pryce portray in that film?

ANSWERS

1, *Toy Story* 2, Jim Carrey 3, Michael Douglas 4, A pig 5, America 6, Tom Hanks 7, Pamela Anderson Lee 8, Val Kilmer 9, Tommy Lee Jones 10, Mel Gibson 11, *Braveheart* 12, Clint Eastwood 13, Pilot (and terrorist) 14, Emma Thompson 15, Lytton Strachey

QUIZ 4

WORLD EVENTS

1 In which post did a Ghanaian replace an Egyptian?

2 Where was Slobodan Milosevic in control?

3 Which German news magazine reached its 50th birthday in 1998?

4 Where did the Grimaldi family celebrate 700 years of rule?

5 What state was headed by Hosni Mubarak?

6 Where was there trouble in Mato Grosso?

7 In which new state was the legislature called the Nitjela?

8 What was Chinabyte?

9 In which city is Skanderbeg Square, a setting for public demonstrations in 1998?

10 What were the protests about?

11 From which country's stamps was the Queen's head removed in 1998?

12 Where was the Truth and Reconciliation Commission working?

13 For whose government did Alistair Campbell 'spin'?

14 In which European country did a paedophile ring scandal break?

15 In which country was ex-premier Bhutto charged with corruption?

ANSWERS

1, UN Secretary General 2, Serbia 3, *Der Spiegel* 4, Monaco 5, Egypt
6, Brazil 7, The Marshall Islands 8, A new Chinese Internet service
9, Albania 10, The collapse of a 'pyramid-selling' scheme 11, Hong Kong
12, South Africa 13, Tony Blair's 14, Belgium 15, Pakistan

QUIZ 5

POT LUCK

1 What was Norman Lamont's last job in government?

2 For whom did David Seaman play soccer?

3 Where was the Pergau Dam?

4 In which TV soap did Kevin and Sally split up?

5 Which veteran singer made the 'Duets' album?

6 Which novelist was a leading Tory crowd-rouser?

7 Who wrote the play *Oleanna* (1992)?

8 Kim Il Sung died in 1994: which country had he led ?

9 Who was Nadja Avermann?

10 A flower's 400th 'birthday 'was celebrated in the Netherlands in 1994. Which flower?

11 Who sang that 'I Wouldn't Normally Do This Kind of Thing'?

12 In which sport did Jamaica win the 1992 Red Stripe Cup?

13 Of which organisation was General Eva Burrows head?

14 What game were the Houston Oilers playing?

15 Which 90s Nobel laureate poet was born in St. Lucia?

ANSWERS

1, Chancellor of the Exchequer 2, Arsenal 3, Malaysia 4, *Coronation Street*
5, Frank Sinatra 6, Jeffrey Archer 7, David Mamet 8, North Korea
9, A German 'super model' 10, The tulip 11, Pet Shop Boys 12, Cricket
13, Salvation Army 14, American Football 15, Derek Walcott

QUIZ 6

PEOPLE

1 Who was called the 'Palestinian's First Lady'?

2 Who was the first Arab secretary-general of the UN?

3 Whom did he replace?

4 And in what year?

5 In which country was B.J. Habibie prominent?

6 And where did Cheryl Kernot make her mark in politics?

7 In which sport was Javed Miandad a star?

8 What is Gary Lineker's middle name?

9 What honour did he receive in 1992?

10 With which band did Eddie Vedder sing?

11 Who saw her 32nd novel *Accident* best-sell in 1994?

12 Lead singer of Nirvana, he killed himself in 1994: who was he?

13 Which Garth sold 50 million albums in the USA during the 90s?

14 And which ex-Spurs Garth could be seen on UK TV?

15 Who became the new leader of Georgia in 1992?

ANSWERS

1, Hanan Ashrawi 2, Boutros Boutros-Ghali 3, Javier Perez de Cuellar 4, 1992 5, Indonesia 6, Australia 7, Cricket 8, Winston 9, Football Writers' Player of the Year 10, Pearl Jam 11, Danielle Steel 12, Kurt Cobain 13, Garth Brooks 14, Garth Crooks 15, Eduard Shevardnadze

QUIZ 7

NAME THE MOVIE STARS

1 Tom H
2 Jim C
3 Robin W
4 Brad P
5 Emma T
6 Mel G
7 Bruce W
8 Kevin C
9 Sylvester S
10 Robert De
11 Dustin H
12 Julia R
13 Meg R
14 Sandra B
15 Michael D

ANSWERS

1, Hanks 2, Carrey 3, Williams 4, Pitt 5, Thompson 6, Gibson 7, Willis
8, Costner 9, Stallone 10, Niro 11, Hoffman 12, Roberts 13, Ryan
14, Bullock 15, Douglas

QUIZ 8

WORLD EVENTS

1 Which Panamanian leader gave himself up?

2 Which country said goodbye to Samuel Doe?

3 Who led the rebels who deposed Doe?

4 Where was Li Peng premier?

5 Which Soviet republic's capital was Vilnius?

6 Who went there to try to stop the republic breaking away?

7 In which country did violence erupt in Baku?

8 Which Bulgarian leader was under arrest?

9 From which country was the ANC outlawed as 1990 began?

10 Who was South Africa's president in 1990?

11 And whom did he free in February of that year?

12 Where did the LDP rule?

13 Of which country was Vaclav Havel president?

14 Where were the Sandinistas beaten in an election?

15 Where was Senator Juan Ponce Enrile arrested?

ANSWERS

1, General Noriega 2, Liberia 3, Charles Taylor 4, China 5, Lithuania 6, Gorbachev 7, Azerbaijan 8, Todor Zhivkov 9, South Africa 10, F.W. de Klerk 11, Nelson Mandela 12, Japan 13, Czechoslovakia 14, Nicaragua 15, The Philippines (for rebellion)

QUIZ 9

PEOPLE

1 Which singer won a Grammy award for 'I'm in the Mood'?

2 Who announced the building of 6 new UK prisons in 1993?

3 Was Julie Krone a) a jockey b) a model c) a writer?

4 Which 90s politicians' initials were J.R.M.?

5 What post did Janet Reno hold from March 1993?

6 Which Jerry wrote a book called *Seinlanguage?*

7 Which Dwight moved to Old Trafford?

8 Whose autobiography was titled *Body and Soul?*

9 Which Austen novel was a big hit on TV?

10 And which Colin starred in it?

11 Which ex-Bond star appeared in the film *Rising Sun?*

12 Which American co-starred with him in this movie?

13 Which former Wimbledon men's champion died in 1993, aged 49?

14 Which D.L. captained the Great Britain Davis Cup team?

15 And in which sport did his namesake run the England show for a while?

ANSWERS

1, John Lee Hooker 2, Michael Howard 3, a) 4, John (Roy) Major 5, US Attorney-General 6, Jerry Seinfeld 7, Dwight York 8, Anita Roddick 9, *Pride and Prejudice* 10, Colin Firth 11, Sean Connery 12, Wesley Snipes 13, Arthur Ashe 14, David Lloyd 15, Cricket

ARTS & ENTERTAINMENT

1 Who or what was Casper?

2 Who was the mayor in the film *City Hall?*

3 Which sport was the subject of the film *Cobb?*

4 Who played the pyschologist heroine of *Copycat?*

5 Was *Cutthroat Island* a) about gangsters b) about pirates or c) about drugs?

6 Who was Sister Helen in *Dead Man Walking?*

7 Who played the killer in this film?

8 Who starred in the *Die Hard* movies?

9 Complete the title: *The Englishman Who Went….?*

10 Who was the anti-terrorist hero of *Executive Decision?*

11 In which film did Richard Gere play Lancelot?

12 And who was King Arthur?

13 What kind of animal was Free Willy?

14 Who played 007 in *Goldeneye?*

15 Who directed the film *In the Bleak Midwinter?*

ANSWERS

1, A ghost 2, Al Pacino 3, Baseball 4, Sigourney Weaver 5, b) 6, Susan Sarandon 7, Sean Penn 8, Bruce Willis 9, *Up a Hill but Came Down a Mountain* 10, Kurt Russell 11, *First Knight* 12, Sean Connery 13, A killer whale 14, Pierce Brosnan 15, Kenneth Branagh

QUIZ 11

WORLD EVENTS

1 Where was Patricio Aylwin president?

2 Which country became the 3rd to send a satellite around the Moon?

3 Under what name did South West Africa become independent?

4 What was the new nation's capital?

5 Where did Bob Hawke get re-elected?

6 Where were the Liberation Tigers fighting a guerrilla war?

7 In which African country did the ZANU (PF) party win power?

8 Which new tax provoked a riot in London?

9 Which leader threatened to annihilate Israel with chemical weapons?

10 Where was Birendra king?

11 Where was Alberto Fujimori campaigning for president?

12 Which country cut off oil supplies to Lithuania?

13 What was global about 22 April 1990?

14 Where did President Babangida rule?

15 Who said he would end one-party rule in Zaire?

ANSWERS

1, Chile 2, Japan 3, Namibia 4, Windhoek 5, Australia 6, Sri Lanka 7, Zimbabwe 8, The poll tax 9, Sadam Hussein 10, Nepal 11, Peru 12, The Soviet Union 13, It was Earth Day 14, Nigeria 15, President Mobutu

QUIZ 12

SPORT

1 Who was the first German Formula One champion driver?

2 For which club did Eric Cantona play before he joined Manchester United?

3 What was Nigel Benn's sport?

4 For which game was the Springold Master Knockout event staged?

5 What is Australian cricketer Shane's surname?

6 What style does he bowl – off-break, fast-medium, or leg-spin?

7 Which London soccer club signed Gianfranco Zola?

8 British drivers finished 2nd and 3rd in the 1995 Formula One drivers' championship. Who were they?

9 In which race did a Reynard-Honda illegally overtake a Chevrolet Corvette, and so lose?

10 At which sport was Devon Malcolm an international?

11 What nationality was Noureddine Morceli?

12 And what sport did he dominate in the early 90s?

13 In which event did he win his 3rd world title in 1995?

14 Which British boxer's career was ended by brain damage in 1991?

15 And who was his opponent in the fateful fight?

ANSWERS

1, Michael Schumacher 2, Leeds United 3, Boxing 4, Contract bridge 5, Warne 6, Leg-spin 7, Chelsea 8, Damon Hill, David Coulthard 9, The 1995 Indianapolis 500 10, Cricket 11, Algerian 12, Athletics 13, 1500 metres 14, Michael Watson 15, Chris Eubank

QUIZ 13

PEOPLE

1 What year did John Major become UK prime minister?

2 Which party did he lead?

3 Whom did he succeed as prime minister?

4 Where was he born: a) Exeter b) London c) Cardiff?

5 Did he go to school at a) a grammar school in Merton b) public school in Gloucester?

6 What is his wife's first name?

7 Is his son's name James, John or Julian?

8 Which war was fought during his premiership?

9 What was his favourite summer game?

10 Whose nomination as President of the European Commission did Major veto in 1994?

11 Which Irish leader did he join in making the Downing Street Declaration?

12 Who challenged Major for the leadership in 1995?

13 Which European treaty split Major's party in 1993?

14 To which region did Major's government direct 'Operation Irma'?

15 What year did Major win the election that won him a new mandate?

ANSWERS

1, 1990 2, Conservative 3, Margaret Thatcher 4, b) 5, a) 6, Norma 7, James 8, The Gulf War 9, Cricket 10, Jean-Luc Dehaene 11, Albert Reynolds 12, John Redwood 13, Maastricht 14, Former Yugoslavia 15, 1992

QUIZ 14

POT LUCK

1 Who played Mr Bean on film and TV?

2 What nationality was the 1996 Nobel Prize-winner for Literature?

3 Where were the 1996 Olympic Games held?

4 Which ex-boxing champion lit the Olympic Flame?

5 Who became Canada's first woman prime minister?

6 Who declared that 'prison works'?

7 Was there really a 90s rap group called Insane Clown Posse?

8 In which country did the LDP lose power after 38 years?

9 What were the Royal Navy's new Vanguards?

10 Who was the number one ranking men's tennis player in 1990?

11 What was the name of the Russian space station?

12 What name was chosen for the new EU currency?

13 Which country was Asia's major coffee grower?

14 For what was Seamus Hearney noted: a) poetry b) comic acting c) film-making?

15 Why were Timothy McVeigh and Terry Nichols arrested in the USA?

ANSWERS

1, Rowan Atkinson 2, Polish (Wislawa Szymborska) 3, Atlanta, Georgia 4, Mohammed Ali 5, Kim Campbell 6, UK Home Secretary Michael Howard 7, Yes 8, Japan 9, Submarines 10, Stefan Edberg 11, Mir 12, Euro 13, Indonesia 14, a) 15, They were charged with the Oklahoma City bombing

QUIZ 15

WORLD EVENTS

1 How many EC countries met at the 1990 EC summit?

2 Of which country was Roh Tae Woo president?

3 How old was Greece's new president Karamanlis?

4 Where did rebels try to capture Antananarivo?

5 Which Balkan state held its first free elections for 50 years?

6 Which two Arab states merged in May1990?

7 Which country apologised to Koreans for its occupation 1910-1945?

8 Who said after a world tour (aged 72) that he felt "like a boy of 36"?

9 Who led the Inkatha organization?

10 And in which country?

11 Where did Shamir form a government?

12 For which affair was John Poindexter sentenced to jail?

13 Where was Violetta Chamorro president in late 1990?

14 Where was Brian Mulroney prime minister?

15 Which Solidarity leader wanted to lead Poland?

ANSWERS

1, Twelve 2, South Korea 3, 83 4, Madagascar 5, Romania 6, North and South Yemen 7, Japan 8, Nelson Mandela 9, Chief Mangosuthu Buthelezi 10, South Africa 11, Israel 12, The 'Iran-contra' affair 13, Nicaragua 14, Canada 15, Lech Walesa

QUIZ 16

PEOPLE

1 What was Dame Peggy Ashcroft's profession?

2 Was Peggy her real name?

3 Was Luke Appling a baseball player or a TV soap star?

4 In which country was Greto Garbo born?

5 In which city did she die in 1990?

6 Which movie actress known for her throaty voice and roles in 1930's comedies died in 1991?

7 In which famous Western did she also star?

8 Her director in several film comedies died the same year. Who was he?

9 Which Japanese carmaker died in 1991?

10 To whom was Paulette Goddard (d. 1990) first married?

11 What did Sir Reginald Goodall (d. 1990) do?

12 Where did James Irvine (d. 1991) walk in 1971?

13 Of which country was Gustav Husak (d. 1991) an ex-ruler?

14 The creator of the Muppets died in 1990. Who was he?

15 What nationality was he?

ANSWERS

1, Actress 2, No (Edith Margaret Emily) 3, US baseball player 4, Sweden
5, New York 6, Jean Arthur 7, *Shane* 8, Frank Capra 9, Soichiro Honda
10, Charlie Chaplin 11, Orchestral Conductor 12, On the Moon
13, Czechoslovakia 14, Jim Henderson 15, American

QUIZ 17

POT LUCK

1 Who made a 1991 album called 'Waking Up the Neighbours'?

2 In which country did UNTAC operate?

3 For what activity was the Carlsberg Prize awarded?

4 Which US orchestra celebrated its 150th birthday in 1992?

5 Who played the US TV character Murphy Brown?

6 Why did Vice President Quayle criticize her character?

7 Is Pierre Boulez a musical conductor or a soccer coach?

8 Who won the woman's 100 metres at the '92 olympics?

9 And her country?

10 By what first name was Labour politician Dr Cunningham usually known?

11 To what post was he appointed in 1992?

12 Which US state did Al Gore represent as senator?

13 Which England soccer star joined Nagoya Grampus Eight?

14 Which Dutch city was the scene of the country's worst-ever air disaster in 1992?

15 In what field was Sir Kenneth MacMillan (died 1992) distinguished?

ANSWERS

1, Bryan Adams 2, Cambodia 3, Architecture 4, New York Philharmonic 5, Candice Bergen 6, Murphy Brown had an illegitimate child 7, A musical conductor 8, Gail Devers 9, USA 10, Jack 11, Shadow Foreign Secretary 12, Tennessee 13, Gary Lineker 14, Amsterdam 15, Ballet

QUIZ 18

WORLD EVENTS

1990

1 Which European state ceased to exist at midnight on 3 October?

2 In which country did Mohawks lay down their arms?

3 In which country did Bush meet Gorbachev in September?

4 Whose body was reburied in Chile?

5 Which lady became Norway's prime minister for the third time?

6 Who became New Zealand's leader a week earlier (end-September)?

7 Which party did this new leader represent?

8 Which European country voted to seek EC membership in December?

9 Where did over 1,000 pilgrims die in a crush?

10 Who shocked Russians by quitting the Communist Party in July?

11 Which Arab leader made his first trip to Egypt since the 70s?

12 Of which city was Marion Barry mayor?

13 And for what crime did he end up in jail?

14 Who finally packed her handbag and resigned in the UK?

15 And which UK political party also announced it was shutting up?

ANSWERS

1. East Germany 2. Canada 3. Finland 4. Salvador Allende 5. Gro Harlem Brundtland 6. Jim Bolger 7. The National Party 8. Sweden 9. Mecca 10. Boris Yeltsin 11. President Assad of Syria 12. Washington, D.C. 13. Cocaine possession 14. Margaret Thatcher 15. The Social Democratic Party

QUIZ 19

SPORT

1 Which defender moved from West Ham to Liverpool for £3m in 1993?

2 Who gave up being Great Britain's rugby league coach in 1994?

3 China won the 1993 Corbillon Cup: which sport?

4 Who were the losers in the 1992 America's Cup races?

5 And who won?

6 In which sport did Park Jang of South Korea win successive world titles in 1992-93?

7 The same two players won the US Open tennis singles titles in 1991and 1992. Who was the man?

8 And who was the woman?

9 Which Asian country won a world ski-jump championship in 1993?

10 In which sport did Canada win a pairs world title in 1993?

11 In which sport did Giant Victory win the 1991 Hambleton Trot?

12 For which sport did Montreal win the 92-93 Stanley Cup?

13 What was the team's full name?

14 Which team were 1991-92 Super Bowl football champions?

15 And whom did they beat?

ANSWERS

1, Julian Dicks 2, Malcolm Reilly 3, Table tennis 4, Italy 5, USA
6, Wrestling 7, Stefan Edberg 8, Monica Seles 9, Japan 10, Figure skating
11, Harness racing 12, Ice hockey 13, Montreal Canadiens
14, Washington Redskins 15, The Buffalo Bills

QUIZ 20

PEOPLE

1 Where was Fidel Ramos chosen President?

2 What agency did Stella Rimington head?

3 Which 'fictional' rock band became real in the early 90s?

4 Who opposed John Smith for the Labour leadership?

5 For what was Isaac Asimov known?

6 Where was Carl Bildt Prime Minister?

7 Of which Commonwealth country was Catherine Tizard governor-general?

8 Where did John Dawkins have charge of the Treasury?

9 What was Hillary Clinton's maiden name?

10 What US government post did William J Perry hold from 1994-97?

11 Was Marian Anderson (died 1993) a famous athlete or singer?

12 What nationality was the actor Cantinflas who also died that year?

13 Which theatre had Sam Wanamaker worked to rebuild?

14 Who wrote the novel *No Other Life?*

15 Who were Ireland's best known rock band of the early 90s?

ANSWERS

1, The Philippines 2, MI-5 3, Spinal Tap 4, Bryan Gould 5, Science Fiction 6, Sweden 7, New Zealand 8, Australia 9, Rodham 10, Secretary of Defence 11, Singer 12, Mexican 13, The Globe 14, Brian Moore 15, U2

QUIZ 21

POT LUCK

1 What language was Gunter Grass writing in?

2 Where was P.V. Narasimha Rao prime minister?

3 Who headed a UK committee on standards of conduct in public life?

4 What was the estimated population of the UK in 1995: a)50 million b)55 million c)58 million?

5 Which new country's capital was Kiev?

6 Which party did Robert Dole represent?

7 Which general declined to run in that election?

8 Who wrote *An Awfully Big Adventure?*

9 In which country was the first Ibsen Stage Festival held?

10 Which yellow puppet starred in a 1999 TV ad?

11 In 1999 who were celebrating 25 years since their Eurovision Song Contest triumph?

12 Which record-breaking mystery play toured the USA in 1990?

13 Which English town celebrated the play-author's centenary?

14 Which country took the America's Cup in 1995?

15 And the score, in races?

ANSWERS

1, German 2, India 3, Lord Nolan 4, c) 5, Ukraine 6, Republican 7, Colin Powell 8, Beryl Bainbridge 9, Norway 10, Flat Eric 11, ABBA 12, *The Mousetrap* 13, Torbay (in honour of Agatha Christie) 14, New Zealand 15, 5-0, defeating the USA

QUIZ 22

PEOPLE

1 Fiona Shaw: actress or politician?

2 Henryck Gorecki: composer or soccer star?

3 Marie Giradelli: fashion designer or ski racer?

4 Annita Keating: writer or politician's wife?

5 Jiang Zemin: political leader or table tennis champ?

6 Jools Holland: musician or TV chef?

7 Cedric Pioline: tennis player or African bishop?

8 Sandra Farmer-Patrick: runner or singer?

9 Alan Curbishley: soccer coach or cricketer?

10 Shannon Miller: golfer or gymnast?

11 Felipe Gonzalez: prime minister or baseball player?

12 Rudolph Giuliani: tycoon or city mayor?

13 Colin Davis: newsreader or orchestra conductor?

14 Iman: Somali model or Brazilian singer?

15 Stephen Hendry: newspaper editor or snooker star?

ANSWERS

1, Actress 2, Composer 3, Ski racer 4, Politician's wife(of Paul Keating) 5, Political leader 6, Musician 7, Tennis player 8, Runner 9, Soccer coach 10, Gymnast 11, Prime Minister 12, City mayor 13, Orchestra conductor 14, Somali model 15, Snooker star

QUIZ 23

ARTS & ENTERTAINMENT

1 Which 1995 film was set in the year 2139?

2 Who was the star who played the comic-book lawman in that film?

3 Who starred in *Jumanji?*

4 Which 1996 film homed in on a mythical Scottish beastie?

5 These Rangers made a movie in 1995: full title please.

6 Where were the Muppets stranded in 1996?

7 Who played a computer bug-hunter in *The Net?*

8 Who was Nixon on screen?

9 In *Primal Fear,* did Richard Gere play a lawyer, a doctor or a soldier?

10 Who played Richard III in a 1995 film?

11 In what era was this version set: 1890s, 1930s or 1990s?

12 Who played Linus Larrabee in *Sabrina?*

13 Complete the film title: *Secrets and ......?*

14 Who played the mother Cynthia in this film?

15 Which Jane Austen novel was filmed by Ang Lee?

ANSWERS

1, *Judge Dredd* 2, Sylvester Stallone 3, Robin Williams 4, *Loch Ness* 5, *Mighty Morphing Power Rangers: The Movie* 6, Muppet Treasure Island 7, Sandra Bullock 8, Anthony Hopkins 9, A lawyer 10, Ian McKellen 11, 1930s 12, Harrison Ford 13, *Lies* 14, Brenda Blethyn 15, *Sense and Sensibility*

QUIZ 24

POT LUCK

1 Where was the Getty Center being built: a)Paris b)Los Angeles c) Moscow?

2 Which London borough was chosen as the site for the Millennium Dome?

3 Where was the Tsing Ma bridge built?

4 In which city did an art exhibition of Charles Rennie Mackintosh's work open in 1996?

5 Which nuclear power station was 40 years old in 1996?

6 In what art-form had Rafael Kubelik been distinguished?

7 In which city did a disco fire kill 159 people (1996)?

8 What meteorological phenomenon upset the 1995 skiing season?

9 What country did Moses Kiptanui run for?

10 Who wrote a poem to the Queen Mother on her 95th birthday?

11 Which war was the setting for the novel *The Ghost Road?*

12 Who wrote it?

13 Which US actor-singer ('The Blue Tailed Fly', etc) died in 1995?

14 In which film had he won an Oscar?

15 Which British newspaper was closed in 1995?

ANSWERS

1, Los Angeles 2, Greenwich 3, Hong Kong 4, Glasgow 5, Calder Hall (UK) 6, Music, as conductor and composer 7, Manila, in the Philippines 8, Warm weather, no snow 9, Kenya 10, Ted Hughes 11, The First World War 12, Pat Barker 13, Burl Ives 14, *The Big Country* 15, *Today*

QUIZ 25

SPORT

1 In which sport did the Searle brothers represent Great Britain?

2 In which sport did the Josephson sisters represent the USA?

3 Which skier was known as 'La Bomba'?

4 What year was the world's first trans-Atlantic balloon race?

5 Which way did the balloons race?

6 Which Briton won the 1992 world motor racing drivers' championship?

7 What car did he drive?

8 In which sport was Eddy Hartono a star?

9 Who beat Graf in the 1st round at the 1994 Wimbledon?

10 Which country did runner Maria Mutola represent?

11 Which British boxer won the WBO heavyweight title in 1994?

12 Which Yorkshire soccer team won promotion to the Premier league?

13 Which club did Kevin Keegan leave in 1999?

14 What was his new job?

15 Which Brazilian racing driver was killed at the 1994 San Mario Grand Prix?

ANSWERS

1, Rowing 2, Synchronized swimming 3, Alberto Tomba 4, 1992 5, East, from the USA to Europe 6, Nigel Mansell 7, Williams-Renault 8, Badminton 9, Lori McNeil (USA) 10, Mozambique 11, Herbie Hide 12, Bradford 13, Fulham 14, England coach 15, Ayrton Senna

QUIZ 26

WORLD EVENTS

1 Was oil production in 1990 higher or lower than in 1970?

2 Which country was the top oil producer in 1990?

3 Which was Western Europe's leading oil producer in 1990?

4 Which country took the USSR's seat in the UN Security Council in 1991?

5 Which European state became two in January 1993?

6 And what names did the two new states take?

7 Which self-proclaimed state had had the initials TRNC since 1983?

8 Where in 1992 did the FMLN sign a deal to end a civil war?

9 Whose 1992 government was led by Flight-Lt Jerry Rawlings?

10 In what Middle Eastern state was martial law (in force since 1967) lifted in 1991?

11 What happened to UK polytechnics under 1992 legislation?

12 Of which country did Oscar Scalfaro become president in 1992?

13 On what date was the UK census taken in the 90s?

14 Who was UK prime minister on 1st January 1991?

15 Where was Ezer Weismann elected president in 1993?

ANSWERS

1, Higher 2, Saudi Arabia 3, The UK 4, Russia 5, Czechoslovakia 6, Czech Republic, Slovakia 7, Turkish Republic of Northern Cyprus 8, El Salvador 9, Ghana 10, Jordan 11, They became universities 12, Italy 13, 21 April 1991 14, John Major 15, Israel

QUIZ 27

PEOPLE

1 What year was Clinton elected President?

2 Which party did he represent?

3 In which US state was he born?

4 Which office had he held before becoming president?

5 Who was his Vice Presidential running mate?

6 Who was the Independent candidate the year Clinton won office?

7 Who served as Clinton's first Secretary of State?

8 And who took over the job in 1997?

9 Which war was ended by the Dayton agreement?

10 Which US domestic system did Clinton seek to reform unsuccessfully in 1993?

11 What post did Janet Reno hold in the Clinton administration?

12 Which 'water' caused the Clintons some embarrassment?

13 Was this a) a land deal b) a sex scandal c) an environmental scare?

14 From which African state did Clinton pull out US troops in 1994?

15 Whom did Clinton defeat to win a second term?

ANSWERS

1, 1992 2, Democratic Party 3, Arkansas 4, Governor of Arkansas
5, Al Gore 6, Ross Perot 7, Warren Christopher 8, Madeleine Albright
9, Bosnian civil war 10, Health care 11, Attorney general 12, Whitewater
13, a) 14, Somalia 15, Bob Dole

QUIZ 28

SPORT

1992 OLYMPICS

1 Where were the 1992 Olympics staged?

2 Which nation won 8 athletics gold medals?

3 In which event did Kevin Young net a world record?

4 Whose record did he beat?

5 Who won the long jump for the 3rd time?

6 Which pole vault favourite failed to place?

7 Which country did William Tanui represent?

8 And which event did he win?

9 Where were the 1992 Winter Olympics staged?

10 In which event did Raisa Smetanina win her 10th Olympic medal?

11 Which European team picked up 5 gold medals for swimming?

12 Which country sent a 13-year-old girl to win gold in the diving?

13 Which British rower won his 3rd gold medal for rowing?

14 Whom did he partner in the coxless pairs?

15 In which sport did Vitali Sherbo win gold?

ANSWERS

1, Barcelona 2, USA 3, 400-m hurdles 4, Ed Moses (1983) 5, Carl Lewis 6, Sergey Bubka 7, Kenya 8, 800-metres 9, France (Albertville) 10, Nordic skiing 11, Hungary 12, China 13, Steve Redgrave 14, Matthew Pinsent 15, Gymnastics

QUIZ 29

POT LUCK

1 Of which magazine was Tina Brown made editor in chief in 1992?

2 Which schoolboy wizard topped the best-selling lists ?

3 Who wrote *Diana: Her True Story?*

4 Which star published a collection of erotic pictures in 1992?

5 The book title?

6 Which explorer's Quincentenary was marked in 1992?

7 What date is officially his day in the USA?

8 Which British soccer team beat Parma to win the 1994 European Cup-Winner's Cup?

9 Which country did Will Carling captain?

10 And in which sport?

11 Which countries were in dispute over the Kuril Islands?

12 Where was the world's largest diamond mine: a) Western Australia b) Brazil c) Sierre Leone?

13 Which Birmingham car plant built Rovers?

14 What nationality was the fast-growing Daewoo car company?

15 What did Clementine fly around in 1994?

ANSWERS

1, *The New Yorker* 2, Harry Potter 3, Andrew Morton 4, Madonna 5, *Sex* 6, Columbus 7, October 12 8, Arsenal 9, England 10, Rugby Union 11, Japan and Russia 12, a) 13, Longbridge 14, South Korean 15, The Moon (it was a small robot spacecraft)

QUIZ 30

ARTS & ENTERTAINMENT

1 Who played Sergeant Bilko on the big screen?

2 Who was the female star of *To Die For?*

3 Who played Mark in *Trainspotting?*

4 Who was Woody's voice in a Disney hit?

5 Who starred in *Waterworld?*

6 What was his character's name?

7 Which *Lion King* characters appeared *Around the World* in their own video?

8 Which collie was still going strong at the age of 370-plus (in human years) ?

9 What kind of animal was *White Fang?*

10 Which US actor-singer died on Christmas Day 1995?

11 Which actor said Hollywood promoted violence?

12 Which actress won an Oscar in 1996 for screenwriting?

13 And the film?

14 Which actor did Melanie Griffith marry in 1996?

15 Who directed the film *Natural Born Killers?*

ANSWERS

1, Steve Martin 2, Nicole Kidman 3, Ewan McGregor 4, Tom Hanks 5, Kevin Costner 6, The Mariner 7, Timon and Pumbaa 8, Lassie 9, A wolf 10, Dean Martin 11, Dustin Hoffman 12, Emma Thompson 13, *Sense and Sensibility* 14, Antonio Banderas 15, Oliver Stone

QUIZ 31

WORLD EVENTS

1 Which British city was hit by an IRA bomb in April?

2 Where was President Premadasa assassinated?

3 Which South American country had its first civilian president since the 1950s?

4 Which African state was officially recognized by the US government?

5 Did Danes vote yes or no to the European Treaty in May?

6 Which Italian art gallery was damaged by a car bomb?

7 In which country was war-torn Mogadishu?

8 Who was still prime minister of Spain?

9 Where did Kim Campbell become the woman in charge?

10 Whose King was Albert II?

11 Whom did he succeed?

12 What job did Ruth Ginsburg take on in the USA?

13 Which country's capital was Abuja (since 1991)?

14 Whose troops left Lithuania?

15 Whose body was returned to the Philippines in September 1993?

ANSWERS

1, London 2, Sri Lanka 3, Paraguay 4, Angola 5, Yes 6, The Uffizi in Florence 7, Somalia 8, Felipe Gonzales 9, Canada 10, Belgium 11, Baudouin I 12, Supreme Court judge 13, Nigeria 14, Russia's 15, Ferdinand Marcos

QUIZ 32

MATCH THE STARS WITH THEIR SPORTS

1 Jana Novotna?

2 Detroit Pistons?

3 Chris Waddle?

4 Kieren Perkins?

5 Wayne Gretzky?

6 Dr Devious?

7 Helen Alfredsson?

8 Nigel Benn?

9 Jimmy White?

10 David Seaman?

11 Jonathan Webb?

12 Sterling Sharpe?

13 Wasim Akram?

14 Wim Jonk?

15 Miguel Indurain

ANSWERS

1, Tennis 2, Basketball 3, Soccer 4, Swimming 5, Ice Hockey 6, Horse racing (a horse!) 7, Golf 8, Boxing 9, Snooker 10, Soccer 11, Rugby Union 12, American Football 13, Cricket 14, Soccer 15, Cycling

QUIZ 33

PEOPLE

1 Which electronics company did Akio Morita (d.1999) co-found?

2 Where was Europe's new Parliament Building opened in 1999?

3 Which food did Forrest Mars (died 1999) develop?

4 Which scientist's portrait featured on UK £20 notes from 1993?

5 Whose image replaced his from 1999?

6 Who was named Hollywood's greatest male star in a 1999 American Film Institute poll?

7 Who was named top female star?

8 He led the Roman Catholic Church in Britain until 1999. Who was he?

9 Who played 'Bones' McCoy in the original *Star Trek?*

10 He died in 1999. What year did he make his debut as 'Bones'?

11 Do you know his character's fictional first name?

12 With which trade was Christina Foyle connected?

13 Where is her famous shop?

14 What monthly event did she found in 1930?

15 He invented the hovercraft. He died in 1999. Who was he?

ANSWERS

1, Sony 2, Strasbourg 3, The Mars bar 4, Michael Faraday 5, Sir Edward Elgar 6, Humphrey Bogart 7, Katherine Hepburn 8, Cardinal Basil Hume 9, DeForest Kelly 10, 1966 11, Leonard 12, Bookselling 13, Charing Cross Road, London 14, A literary luncheon 15, Sir Christopher Cockerell

QUIZ 34

POT LUCK

1 Which doll was 35 years old in 1994?

2 Which rival doll was the subject of a 1991 'copycat' lawsuit?

3 Which Muslim country banned the doll?

4 Who resigned as director of Kenya Wildlife Service in 1994?

5 What accident had befallen him the year before?

6 What was Reba McEntire's musical style?

7 Where was an unusual shadow-clock installed in a railway station ceiling?

8 Who stood down as Labour's deputy leader after the '92 general election?

9 Which country's cattle herd seemed to be growing the fastest in the mid '90s?

10 What was *Australopithecus afarensis*, whose bones were being found in Africa?

11 In which city was a 1953 McDonald's 'Golden Arch' damaged by earthquake?

12 Who was 'Otzi the Iceman'?

13 Which Commonwealth leader suggested in 1992 that his country needed a new flag?

14 Who lost his seat in Parliament and then went to Hong Kong?

15 Which famous humorous magazine closed in 1992?

ANSWERS

1, Barbie 2, Miss America 3, Kuwait 4, Richard Leakey 5, A plane crash in which he lost both legs 6, Country and Western 7, New York 8, Roy Hattersley 9, China's 10, An early hominid ('ape-man') 11, Los Angeles 12, A frozen body found in the Alps in 1992 13, Australian prime minister Paul Keating 14, Chris Patten 15, *Punch*

QUIZ 35

WORLD EVENTS

1992

1 Which world organisation had a new boss?

2 Which new state's capital was Tbilisi?

3 Where did President Bendjedid resign?

4 Which Central American civil war ended after 15 years?

5 In which country was Nairobi a centre of protest?

6 Where did President Zhelev win an election?

7 Which Irish prime minister quit?

8 Who replaced him?

9 Where was former President Ershad in jail?

10 There was trouble in Caracas: which country?

11 What did the initials CIS stand for?

12 Who had formed it?

13 Where were the Winter Olympic Games ending in February 1992?

14 Which country had competed as one team for the first time since 1964?

15 Where was Fahd King?

ANSWERS

1, The United Nations 2, Georgia 3, Algeria 4, El Salvador's 5, Kenya 6, Algeria 7, Charles Haughey 8, Albert Reynolds 9, Bangladesh 10, Venezuela 11, Commonwealth of Independent States 12, Eleven ex-Soviet republics 13, Albertville, France 14, Germany 15, Saudi Arabia

QUIZ 36

PEOPLE

THEY ALL DIED IN THE 1990S

1 With which TV series was Gene Roddenberry associated?

2 Was Magnus Pyke a scientist or a politician?

3 Which throne did Prince Vladinir Romanov claim?

4 What TV show did Christopher Trace present?

5 What kind of books did Rosemary Sutcliff write?

6 In which country did Margot Fonteyn die?

7 With which sport was Freddie Brown connected?

8 Who wrote about Willy Wonka?

9 In which film did Ian Charleson play an Olympic runner?

10 In which Western TV series had Michael Landon made his name?

11 Which member of the 'Rat Pack' died in May 1991?

12 What was Rocky Graziano's sport?

13 The boss of Occidental Petroleum died in 1990. Who was he?

14 What nationality was singer Elizabeth Harwood?

15 Mikhail Tal (d. 1992) was an expert at what?

ANSWERS

1, *Star Trek* 2, Scientist 3, Russian 4, *Blue Peter* 5, Historical Fiction 6, Panama 7, Cricket 8, Roald Dahl 9, *Chariots of Fire* 10, *Bonanza* and *Little House on the Prairie* 11, Sammy Davies Jr 12, Boxing 13, Armand Hammer 14, British 15, Chess (former world champion)

SPORT

TENNIS

1 Which Jim won 2 out of 4 grand slam titles in 1992?

2 Which titles eluded him?

3 Who won the 1992 women's singles at Wimbledon?

4 She beat the then number one, who was...?

5 In 1993 who was men's singles champion at Wimbledon?

6 A European team won the Davis Cup in 1991 - which?

7 What nationality was Gabriella Sabatini?

8 Which Czech-born player won the 1990 Australian title?

9 Who partnered Mark Woodforde in a notable doubles team?

10 Which Spaniard won the French singles title in 1993 and 1994?

11 Who made her last Wimbledon appearance in 1994?

12 Who beat her in her last final?

13 What nationality was Michael Stich?

14 What year did he win Wimbledon?

15 Whom did he beat in the final?

ANSWERS

1, Courier 2, Wimbledon, US 3, Steffi Graf 4, Monica Seles 5, Pete Sampras 6, France 7, Argentine 8, Ivan Lendl 9, Todd Woodbridge 10, Sergi Bruguera 11, Martina Navratilova 12, Conchita Martinez 13, German 14, 1991 15, Boris Becker

QUIZ 38

PEOPLE

COMPLETE THE NAMES

1 Tennis star Tim?
2 Royal partner Camilla?
3 Presidential aide Monica?
4 Russian boss Boris?
5 England rugby player Matt?
6 Man Utd goalkeeper Peter?
7 Bill the 'comeback kid'?
8 Balloonist-tycoon Richard?
9 Northern Ireland peace-seeker Mo?
10 Smash-hit singer Robbie?
11 Jerry wife of Mick?
12 Footballer Stan who had a spat with Ulrika?
13 Knighted bachelor boy Sir Cliff?
14 Retiring South African President Nelson?
15 Writer Salman, still under threat?

ANSWERS

1, Henman 2, Parker-Bowles 3, Lewinsky 4, Yeltsin 5, Dawson
6, Schmeichel 7, Clinton 8, Branson 9, Mowlam 10, Williams 11, Hall
12, Collymore 13, Richard 14, Mandela 15, Rushdie

WORLD EVENTS

1 Which two African countries' presidents died in the same 1994 air crash?

2 Which former US President died of a stroke in April?

3 Which evangelist led the funeral service?

4 Where was the Zapatista National Liberation Army active?

5 Where were the worst bush fires in 200 years raging in January 1994?

6 Which US city was hit by an earthquake?

7 Which country's president was Leonid Kravchuk?

8 Which three countries were accepted as EU members (from 1995)?

9 For which 1993 terrorist bombing were four men convicted in the USA?

10 Which church ordained its first women priests?

11 Who was chairman of the PLO?

12 Which French president watched the first Eurotunnel trains depart?

13 Who headed the UK party for the official opening of the tunnel?

14 Where was a new whale sanctuary set up?

15 Who was charged in Los Angeles with murdering his wife Nicole?

ANSWERS

1, Burundi and Rwanda 2, Richard Nixon 3, Billy Graham 4, Mexico 5, New South Wales, Australia 6, Los Angeles 7, Ukraine 8, Austria, Finland, Sweden 9, World Trade Center, New York 10, Church of England 11, Yasir Arafat 12, Francois Mitterand 13, The Queen 14, The Antarctic 15, O J Simpson

QUIZ 40

ARTS & ENTERTAINMENT

1 Who played the President in the 1996 film *Mars Attacks?*

2 In which 1991 comedy did Sylvester Stallone play a gangster trying to go straight?

3 Which King's madness was the focus for a 1994 film?

4 Who played the King?

5 And what was the film's title?

6 Was *Crimson Tide* a) a thriller b) a musical c) a nature film?

7 Was it about a) a submarine b) a basketball team c) a fishing boat?

8 Which rap artist starred in the movie *Juice?*

9 In which film of a Hardy novel did Catherine Zeta Jones play Eustacia Vye?

10 Who played the mobster Ace in the 1995 movie *Casino?*

11 In *Fievel Goes West,* what kind of creature was Fievel?

12 Which John starred in *Look Who's Talking Now?*

13 Who was *The Fugitive* in the 1993 movie?

14 Who co-starred in *A Perfect Murder* (1998)?

15 Of which 1954 film was it a remake?

ANSWERS

1, Jack Nicholson 2, *Oscar* 3, George III 4, Nigel Hawthorne 5, *The Madness of King George* 6, a) 7, a) 8, Tupac Shakur 9, *Return Of the Native* 10, Robert De Niro 11, A mouse 12, Travolta 13, Harrison Ford 14, Gwyneth Paltrow and Michael Douglas 15, *Dial M For Murder*

QUIZ 41

PEOPLE

THEY ALL DIED IN 1993

1 A King of Belgium?

2 A British socialite noted for her scandalous love-life?

3 The actor who played Perry Mason?

4 A trumpeter nicknamed Dizzy?

5 A miners' leader from Lancashire?

6 An actor once married to Jean Simmons?

7 Probably the world's most famous dancer?

8 A Tory politician who'd resigned in 1990 for being rude to the Germans?

9 Founder of a famous US prize for journalism?

10 President of the ANC until 1991?

11 Italian film-maker Federico?

12 West Ham and England soccer star?

13 American actress who co-starred in *The Thin Man?*

14 Outspoken Labour MP Ian?

15 Willie the wizz of the pool table?

ANSWERS

1, Baudouin I 2, Margaret, Duchess of Argyll 3, Raymond Burr 4, John Birks Gillespie 5, Joe Gormley 6, Stewart Granger 7, Rudolf Nureyev 8, Nicholas Ridley 9, Joseph Pulitzer 10, Oliver Tambo 11, Fellini 12, Bobby Moore 13, Myrna Loy 14, Mikardo 15, Mosconi

QUIZ 42

POT LUCK

1 Whose nickname was 'Slick Willy'?

2 Which Royal had a hip replacement in 1998?

3 Where was Carla Tucker executed?

4 Who was chairman of microsoft?

5 What was QVC?

6 What post did Lord Irvine hold in the UK?

7 In which TV show did Pamela Anderson make her name?

8 With which band did her husband perform?

9 And his name?

10 Who led Ulster's Unionists as the decade ended ?

11 Which country was hit by Hurricane George?

12 Which Italian city was hit by a mudslide in 1998?

13 Which pop singer was arrested in Los Angeles for a 'lewd act'?

14 Who or what was Dolly the sheep?

15 Who was torn between Anthea and Della?

ANSWERS

1, President Clinton 2, The Queen Mother 3, Texas, USA 4, Bill Gates 5, A US shopping channel 6, Lord Chancellor 7, *Baywatch* 8, Motley Crue 9, Tommy Lee 10, David Trimble 11, The USA (especially Florida) 12, Naples 13, George Michael 14, The first cloned adult mammal 15, Grant Bovey

QUIZ 43

ARTS & ENTERTAINMENT

1 Which Bart hit the TV screens?

2 Which country had the most TV sets in 1990?

3 Which theatre company turned its back on the Barbican?

4 Which ex-*Dynasty* star appeared on stage in a Noel Coward play in 1990?

5 And the play?

6 What was Twyla Sharp's Brief Fling?

7 What instrument did Rostropovich play?

8 Which UK composer was 85 in 1990?

9 Were Public Enemy a) a punk band b) a rap group

10 Which African politician turned up at a Wembley concert in his honour in 1990?

11 Which Sarah (jazz singer) died in 1990?

12 Who wrote *Rabbit At Rest?*

13 Which 'queen of the mystery' would have been 100 in 1990?

14 Which actor played her Belgian detective on TV?

15 And the sleuth's name?

ANSWERS

1, Bart Simpson 2, The USA (about 200 million) 3, The RSC 4, Joan Collins 5, *Private Lives* 6, A new ballet 7, Cello 8, Michael Tippett 9, b) 10, Nelson Mandela 11, Sarah Vaughan 12, John Updike 13, Agatha Christie 14, David Suchet 15, Hercule Poirot

QUIZ 44

WORLD EVENTS

1 Where was the news magazine *De Tik* suppressed?

2 Which event was marked by a 50th anniversary commemoration in France in June 1994?

3 In which country was the Muslim Brotherhood active?

4 Which international body held elections for 567 seats?

5 Who or what was the PNA?

6 Who became its first head in July?

7 Where were Tutsi and Hutu fighting?

8 To which neighbouring country did 2 million refugees flee?

9 Which was the world's biggest airline?

10 Who bought a controlling interest in it in 1994?

11 Who was chosen to lead the UK Labour Party in July '94?

12 Where was Sir Dawda Jawara overthrown?

13 And where did Wim Kok take over?

14 From where were refugees seeking to enter the USA in small boats and rafts?

15 What issue did a UN conference in Cairo discuss?

ANSWERS

1, Indonesia 2, The D-Day landing of 1944 3, Egypt 4, The European Parliament 5, Palestinian National Authority 6, Yasir Arafat 7, Rwanda 8, Zaire 9, United Airlines 10, Its employees 11, Tony Blair 12, The Gambia 13, The Netherlands 14, Cuba 15, Population control

QUIZ 45

POT LUCK

1 A 90s 'celebrity'-: Denise --- ----- . Who?

2 Who lost his job as England soccer coach in 1999?

3 Who or what was Dana International?

4 Who decided to run for London mayor and get back the top job in the city after 14 years?

5 Which newspaper portrayed the Tory leader as a parrot upside-down?

6 Who was the Tory leader?

7 Who was Theodore Kaczynski, jailed in the USA?

8 Which Labour minister was 'outed' in 1998?

9 Who had iced water thrown at him at the Brit Awards?

10 To whom did James Major become engaged, and marry?

11 Where were Deborah Parry and Lucille McLauchlan jailed?

12 Who got into trouble for spending £600,000 on new wallpaper and decorations in his Westminster home?

13 Which former cricket star was in court in France?

14 In which French city did English soccer fans riot in 1998?

15 Who left Ali Cockayne?

ANSWERS

1, Van Outen 2, Glen Hoddle 3, The Israeli winner of the 1998 Eurovision Song contest 4, Ken Livingstone 5, *The Sun* 6, William Hague 7, The so-called 'Una Bomber' 8, Peter Mandelson 9, John Prescott 10, Emma Noble 11, Saudi Arabia 12, The Lord Chancellor 13, Geoff Boycott 14, Marseilles 15, Will Carling

QUIZ 46

PEOPLE

1 Which novelist was the niece of a Chilean president?

2 Who was Iceland's most famous pop singer?

3 In which country was Antonio Banderas born?

4 In which 1993 film did he co-star with Tom Hanks?

5 With what business was Charles Scribner connected?

6 Of which city was Jacques Chirac mayor?

7 What does Darcey Bussell do?

8 Who partnered Dawn French on TV?

9 What was New Zealand's 'Black Magic'?

10 And what did it win?

11 Which German building was wrapped in fabric for art's sake?

12 In which musical did the character Norma Desmond feature?

13 Which actress won a 1995 Tony award for playing her?

14 In which country was Phoolan Devi a folk-hero?

15 What had she been before being 'reborn' (and released from jail)?

ANSWERS

1, Isabel Allende 2, Bjork 3, Spain 4, Philadelphia 5, Book publishing 6, Paris 7, Dance 8, Jennifer Saunders 9, A yacht 10, The America's Cup 11, The Reichstag in Berlin 12, *Sunset Boulevard* 13, Glenn Close 14, India 15, A bandit leader

QUIZ 47

ARTS & ENTERTAINMENT

1 In which British city was the Citizens' Theatre active?

2 Which composer's 6th symphony was first heard in 1996?

3 Which conductor of the same surname led the 'Last Night of the Proms'?

4 What jazz trumpeter was remembered in a new museum in New York?

5 Who recorded a hit US album called 'The Score'?

6 Which top British band from Manchester cut short a 1996 US tour?

7 Which member of the band chose to watch one 1996 concert from the audience?

8 What kind of music was heard at New York's JVC Festival?

9 Name the 'Three Tenors': the small one?

10 The Italian?

11 The other one?

12 Which famous choir had its first female conductor?

13 Whose 15-hour-long opera cycle hit Chicago in 1996?

14 Which American screen dancer died in 1996?

15 In which famous 1952 musical had he got rather wet?

ANSWERS

1, Glasgow 2, Peter Maxwell Davies 3, Andrew Davies 4, Louis Armstrong 5, The Fugees, or Refugee Camp 6, Oasis 7, Liam Gallagher 8, Jazz 9, José Carreras 10, Luciano Pavarotti 11, Placido Domingo 12, The Vienna Boys Choir 13, *The Ring* by Wagner 14, Gene Kelly 15, *Singin' in The Rain*

QUIZ 48

PEOPLE

1 The widow of Rajiv?

2 The governor of the Bank of England from 1993?

3 The Newt in the US Home of Representatives?

4 The so-called 'King of rai music'.

5 The fastest man in the world over 200 and 400 metres?

6 The King of Cambodia in 1993?

7 UK Employment secretary in 1990?

8 'Mad Merv' the cricketer from Melbourne?

9 He joined Ferrari as top driver in 1996?

10 Deputy leader of the Labour Party from 1994?

11 Maker of films such as *If* (1968), he died in 1994.

12 Novelist A. N. -------?

13 She was stabbed by a fan during a tennis match in Germany.

14 Carlos led Argentina, as president?

15 American fashion designer, Donna------?

ANSWERS

1, Sonia Gandhi 2, Eddie George 3, Newt Gingrich 4, Khaled 5, Michael Johnson 6, Norodom Sihanouk 7, Michael Howard 8, Mervyn Hughes 9, Michael Schumacher 10, John Prescott 11, Lindsay Anderson 12, Wilson 13, Monica Seles 14, Carlos Menem 15, Karan

QUIZ 49

SPORT

GOLF

1 Where was the 1993 Ryder Cup played?

2 Which team won?

3 They had last won on British soil in 1982: true or false?

4 Which Lee won the 1993 US Open?

5 The British Open that year was won by an Australian: who?

6 On which S. Carolina course did the USA win the 1991 Ryder Cup?

7 Which Bernard captained Britain and Europe?

8 Who won the US Open in 1991 for the third time?

9 What was unusual about Phil Mickelson's golf?

10 What is the women's equivalent of the Ryder Cup?

11 Which team had a surprise win in this event in 1992?

12 Which Laura was a rising star in women's golf?

13 Which team won the first Sunrise world team championship in 1992?

14 Was this a men's or women's event?

15 Who won his first major title in 1992 at Augusta?

ANSWERS

1, The Belfry 2, The USA 3, True 4, Lee Janzen 5, Greg Norman 6, Kiawah Island 7, Gallacher 8, Hale Irwin 9, He was left-handed 10, The Solheim Cup 11, Europe 12, Laura Davies 13, Sweden 14, Women's 15, Fred Couples (US Masters)

QUIZ 50

PEOPLE

ALL DIED 1993

1 Name the actress who starred in the film *My Fair Lady* (1964) and died in 1993?

2 In which country was she born?

3 In what game did Lindsay Hassett captain his country?

4 And the country?

5 Which UK party did Jo Grimond formerly lead?

6 In which 70s scandal had H R Halderman been involved?

7 Which veteran US actress had a New York theatre named after her?

8 In which country did Rudolf Nureyev die?

9 Which former US First Lady died in 1993?

10 By what name was singer Harold Lloyd Jenkins known in the 60s and 70s?

11 A 'Mother of Invention', this rock musician died 1993. Who was he?

12 Was Bruno Pontecorvo a scientist, a gangster or a former Pope?

13 By what first name was Lord Zuckerman usually known?

14 Was he a comedian, a scientist or a supermarket boss?

15 With which sport was Danie Craven associated?

ANSWERS

1, Audrey Hepburn 2, Belgium 3, Cricket 4, Australia 5, Liberal
6, Watergate 7, Helen Hayes 8, France 9, Pat Nixon 10, Conway Twitty
11, Frank Zappa 12, A scientist 13, Solly 14, A scientist 15, Rugby Union

QUIZ 51

ART & ENTERTAINMENT

1 Who wrote the novel *We Were The Mulvaneys?*

2 Which poet published *The Spirit Level?*

3 Which writer wrote *Independence Day?*

4 Whose autobiography was called *Before The Dawn?*

5 Which reference set went on sale for £4,900 in Britain?

6 Which ex-politician wrote a novel called *A Woman's Place?*

7 Who wrote his 26th novel, *Vanishing Point* (1996)?

8 Whose play *The Trials of Brother Jero* got him into trouble in Nigeria?

9 Who wrote the play *The Madness of George III?*

10 And who wrote the play *Pentecost* (1994)?

11 Was *Rent* a novel or a musical?

12 Which 19th century opera did it update?

13 Which painter did Antony Sher portray on stage?

14 And who starred in London as John Gabriel Borkman?

15 In the play of that name by ------- who?

ANSWERS

1, Joyce Carol Oates 2, Seamus Heaney 3, Richard Ford 4, Gerry Adams 5, Macmillan's *Dictionary of Art* 6, Edwina Curry 7, Morris West 8, Wole Soyinka 9, Alan Bennett 10, David Hare 11, A musical 12, *La Boheme* 13, Stanley Spencer 14, Paul Scofield 15, Henrik Ibsen

QUIZ 52

POT LUCK

1 Which Rolling Stone had a marital tiff in 1998?

2 What coveted trophy did Jana Novotna finally win?

3 Who marched at Drumcree?

4 From whom did Bruce Willis say he was parting (1998)?

5 Who held his 50th birthday bash at Highgrove in 1998?

6 For whom had David Shayler once worked?

7 Which animals on the run became celebrities in Wiltshire?

8 Which new pill gave a lift to men in 1998?

9 Which murderer was cleared 45 years after he was hanged?

10 Who went back into space 26 years on?

11 How old was he?

12 Which country tested its new Ghand missile?

13 What was the score in the 1998 World Cup Final?

14 Who beat who?

15 Who married Grace Machel?

ANSWERS

1, Mick Jagger 2, The Wimbledon ladies singles 3, Northern Ireland Orangemen 4, Demi Moore 5, Prince Charles 6, MI-5 7, Two Tamworth pigs 8, Viagra 9, Derek Bentley 10, John Glenn 11, 77 12, Pakistan 13, 3-0 14, France beat Brazil 15, Nelson Mandela

QUIZ 53

PEOPLE

1 Which ex-US Vice President died in 1996?

2 Where was Isabelle Huppert born?

3 Which British Queen did she portray in a 1996 play?

4 Was Damien Hirst in the news for a) art b) singing c) motor racing?

5 For what was John Galliano famous?

6 Which royal had a 70th birthday in 1996?

7 Which Irish swimmer won gold in the water but then came under suspicion?

8 What was 'Beverly Hills 90210': a hospital, a high school, or a police precinct?

9 Who wrote the novel *Beside The Ocean Of Time?*

10 On which islands did he live?

11 Which producer of James Bond films died in 1996?

12 What was the last Bond film he saw made (1995)?

13 In which sport had René Lacoste been a star?

14 Which Premiership soccer team did David O'Leary manage?

15 And at which club did his former boss George Graham take over the reins?

ANSWERS

1, Spiro Agnew 2, Paris 3, Mary Stuart (Mary Queen of Scots) 4, a) 5, Fashion design 6, Queen Elizabeth II 7, Michelle Smith 8, A high school 9, George Mackay Brown 10, The Orkneys 11, 'Cubby' Broccoli 12, *Goldeneye* 13, Tennis 14, Leeds United 15, Tottenham Hotspur

QUIZ 54

POT LUCK

1 Which club finally allowed women in?

2 From which film did the song 'You Can Keep Your Hat On' come?

3 Which lady from *The Cruise* became a singing star?

4 In which TV series did Calista Flockhart make her name?

5 Which actress appeared in *The Blue Room?*

6 Which ex-soccer player appeared in *Lock, Stock And Two Smoking Barrels?*

7 Which Chilean general came to London and stayed a while?

8 Which government minister did 'something foolish' on Clapham Common'?

9 From which post did he resign?

10 For what was Marco Pierre White famous?

11 With which pop duo did Neil Tennant sing?

12 Who married Lili Maltese in 1998?

13 Whom did Jim Threapleton marry the same year?

14 With whom did Melanie Blatt sing?

15 Who sacked Lord Cranbourne?

ANSWERS

1, The MCC 2, *The Full Monty* 3, Jane McDonald 4, *Ally McBeal* 5, Nicole Kidman 6, Vinnie Jones 7, General Pinochet 8, Ron Davies 9, Welsh Secretary 10, Cooking 11, Pet Shop Boys 12, Henry Dent Brocklehurst 13, Kate Winslet 14, All Saints 15, William Hague

QUIZ 55

SPORT

NAME THE STARS

1 Wade D---? (rugby)
2 Tom K---? (golf)
3 Tony A---? (bowls)
4 Bonnie B---? ice skating)
5 Evelyn A---? (athletics)
6 Steve J---? (marathon runner)
7 Riddick B---? (boxing)
8 Greg L---? (cycling)
9 Walter S---? (horse racing)
10 Michael J---? (basketball)
11 Brian L---? (cricket)
12 Michael A---? (cricket)
13 Nigel M---? (car racing)
14 Stephen H---? (snooker)
15 Greg N---? (golf)

ANSWERS

1, Dooley 2, Kite 3, Allcock 4, Blair 5, Ashford 6, Jones 7, Bowe 8, LeMond 9, Swinburne 10, Jordan 11, Lara 12, Atherton 13, Mansell 14, Hendry 15, Norman

QUIZ 56

PEOPLE

COMPLETE THE NAMES

1 Alanis M---, Canadian singer.
2 Robin C-----, British Foreign Secretary.
3 Steven R----, British rower.
4 Jonah L-----, All Black rugby player.
5 Lennox L---, world boxing champ.
6 Liam and Noel---, Oasis brothers.
7 Robert M---, Zimbabwean leader.
8 Mike A----, England cricket captain.
9 Susan S----, Oscar-winning US actress.
10 Kevin K---, soccer manager.
11 Bob D-----, losing US presidential runner.
12 Mikhail G----- , reformer of the old USSR.
13 Helmut K-----, German leader.
14 Cilla B-----, TV presenter.
15 Hugh G----, floppy-haired actor.

ANSWERS

1, Morisette 2, Cook 3, Redgrave 4, Lomu 5, Lewis 6, Gallagher
7, Mugabe 8, Atherton 9, Sarandon 10, Keegan 11, Dole 12, Gorbachev
13, Kohl 14, Black 15, Grant

QUIZ 57

POT LUCK

1 Who said in 1998 'the time to stop the killing is now, before it spreads'?

2 Of which troublespot was he/she speaking?

3 Which country told tourists not to kiss publicly?

4 Which princess suffered a stroke on Mustique?

5 Whom did Manchester United beat to win the European Champions Cup in 1999?

6 Of which country was Jigme Singye Wangchuk king?

7 Who said he thought stability was a 'sexy thing'?

8 Who ate cabbage pie on his 67th birthday?

9 Who said he was 'pissed off trying to make this thing work'?

10 Where was TV banned by the new government?

11 Which rugby nation was invited to turn 5 into 6?

12 Who was called a 'sad figure locked in the past' by a party colleague?

13 Who made the remark?

14 Which Sussex town was struck by a tornado in 1998?

15 Which wrestling giant died in 1998?

ANSWERS

1, Madeline Albright 2, Kosovo 3, India 4, Princess Margaret 5, Bayern Munich 6, Bhutan 7, Tony Blair 8, Boris Yeltsin 9, Gerry Adams (of the N. Ireland peace talks) 10, Afghanistan 11, Italy 12, Edward Heath 13, William Hague 14, Selsey 15, Giant Haystacks

QUIZ 58

ARTS & ENTERTAINMENT

1 Which institution is the subject of the play *Racing Demon?*

2 At which Sussex theatre was the play staged in 1998?

3 Whose new musical was *Whistle Down The Wind?*

4 US actor Kevin S----- had a good year in 1998. His name?

5 In which play did he appear in London?

6 Which 'ex-Trainspotter' turned to waving a light-sabre?

7 Which musical revival was a 1998 hit at London's National Theatre?

8 With which pop band did Jarvis Cocker sing?

9 From which country did Aqua hail?

10 How many weddings in the 1994 hit movie title?

11 In which country was Disney's *Mulan* set?

12 Which Private was 'saved' in a 1998 film?

13 Which war was it set in?

14 Who won a BAFTA award for her role in *The Ice Storm?*

15 Who directed and starred in the film *Bulworth?*

ANSWERS

1, The Church of England 2, Chichester Festival Theatre 3, Andrew Lloyd Webber 4, Kevin Spacey 5, *The Iceman Cometh* 6, Ewan McGregor 7, *Oklahoma!* 8, Pulp 9, Denmark 10, Four 11, China 12, Ryan in *Saving Private Ryan* 13, World War II 14, Sigourney Weaver 15, Warren Beatty

QUIZ 59

PEOPLE

1 One of Burl Ives' names was Ivanhoe: true or false?

2 One of his hit songs was 'Frosty the Snowman': true or false?

3 Rose Kennedy died in 1995: whose widow was she?

4 How old was she when she died?

5 Who was her most famous child?

6 For which country did Sachin Tendulkar play cricket?

7 How old was he when made captain?

8 What did Star TV want to do in 1996, but Tendulkar said no?

9 In what sport was Marie-José Perec a star?

10 What rare double did she achieve in 1996?

11 Was she American, Czech or French?

12 In which country did voters choose 'Bibi'?

13 What was his full name?

14 What game did Mickey Mantle grace?

15 In which 90s year did he die?

ANSWERS

1, True 2, True 3, Joseph P. Kennedy 4, 104 5, President John F. Kennedy 6, India 7, 23 8, Televise his marriage 9, Athletics 10, Golds at 200m and 400m in the Olympics 11, French 12, Israel 13, Benjamin Netanyahu 14, Baseball 15, 1995

QUIZ 60

ARTS & ENTERTAINMENT

1 In which TV comedy series did Martin Clunes star?
2 What was Channel 4's early morning show?
3 Which penguin was a children's favourite?
4 Which Scottish footballer was a *Question of Sport* captain?
5 Which children's TV series featured Dick and Julian as two of five?
6 What sport did Mark Nicholas present on TV?
7 Which veteran GP commentator was still talking fast on a different channel?
8 What kind of show did the two fat ladies present?
9 Which science programme looked beyond today?
10 Which quiz-show wheel was still turning?
11 Who showed viewers 'Auntie's Bloomers'?
12 Which programmes about collies stirred up emotions?
13 Who or what was Sabrina on children's TV?
14 Who made her name on *Ground Force?*
15 Which children's show was set in Cackle's Academy?

ANSWERS

1, *Men Behaving Badly* 2, *The Big Breakfast* 3, Pingu 4, Ally McCoist 5, *The Famous Five* 6, Cricket 7, Murray Walker 8, Cooking 9, *Tomorrow's World* 10, *Wheel of Fortune* 11, Terry Wogan 12, *One Man And His Dog* 13, *The Teenage Witch* 14, Charlie Dimmock 15, *The Worst Witch*

QUIZ 61

SPORT

SOCCER

1 Which French team did Raymond Goethals coach?

2 Which England World Cup hero died in 1993?

3 What experimentally replaced the throw-in for certain games?

4 Which country launched its first professional soccer league in 1993?

5 Which country's national team died in a 1993 air disaster?

6 From which country did Hristo Stoichkov play?

7 For which club did he and Ronald Koeman play in the 1992 European Champions' cup final?

8 The match was played in the UK: where?

9 Who won?

10 Who scored Denmark's first goal in the 1992 European Championship?

11 What was the final score?

12 And whom did Denmark beat?

13 Which star striker left Southampton for Blackburn in 1992?

14 Of which European club was Silvio Berlusconi president?

15 In which country did Besiktas play undefeated in 1991-92?

ANSWERS

1, Marseille 2, Bobby Moore 3, The kick-in 4, Japan 5, Zambia 6, Bulgaria 7, Barcelona 8, Wembley 9, Barcelona beat Sampdoria 1-0 10, John Jensen 11, 2-0 12, Germany 13, Alan Shearer 14, AC Milan 15, Turkey

QUIZ 62

PEOPLE

ALL DIED 1998

1 Broadcaster and comedy writer F.M?

2 Controversial politician E.P?

3 Cowboy star R.R?

4 'Tosh' from *The Bill*: K.L?

5 TV's Miss Marple: J.H?

6 Actor who starred in *Planet of the Apes:* R.M?

7 Country singer T.W?

8 Satirist J.W?

9 Creator of Alf Garnett, writer J.S?

10 Olympic superstar F.G.J?

11 Photographer and promoter of vegetarian foods L.M?

12 Novelist C.C?

13 Cartoonist who gave us Andy Capp: R.S?

14 'Father Ted' on TV, actor D.M.?

15 Broadcaster, jazzman and cricket-lover B.G?

ANSWERS

1, Frank Muir 2, Enoch Powell 3, Roy Rogers 4, Kevin Lloyd 5, Joan Hickson 6, Roddy McDowell 7, Tammy Wynette 8, John Wells 9, Johnny Speight 10, Florence Griffith Joyner 11, Linda McCartney 12, Catherine Cookson 13, Reg Smythe 14, Dermot Morgan 15, Benny Green

QUIZ 63

POT LUCK

1 Which national leader announced his retirement on New Year's Eve 1999?

2 Which UK politician said goodbye to Health to campaign in London?

3 Which veteran football manager went home to rescue the Magpies?

4 What prize did José Saramayo win?

5 Which river was to have a new pedestrian-only bridge for the Millennium?

6 Who became Labour's new Home Secretary in 1997?

7 Who became the highest-paid woman on British TV?

8 On which show had her maths wizardry made her a celebrity?

9 Who wrote a book called *Charles: Victim or Villain?*

10 From which TV show was Richard Bacon sacked?

11 Which Northern Irish politicians won the Nobel Peace Prize?

12 Which Spice Girl went solo?

13 Which Spice Girl married a soccer star?

14 And his name?

15 Which toy on a string became a hit again with kids?

ANSWERS

1, Boris Yeltsin 2, Frank Dobson 3, Bobby Robson 4, Nobel Prize for Literature 5, The Thames in London 6, Jack Straw 7, Carol Vorderman 8, *Countdown* 9, Penny Junor 10, *Blue Peter* 11, David Trimble and John Hume 12, Ginger (Geri Halliwell) 13, Posh (Victoria Adams) 14, David Beckham 15, The yo-yo

QUIZ 64

WORLD EVENTS

1 Where did 75 of 87 visiting Chinese defect in 1995?

2 Where was Markus Wolf convicted of treason?

3 Who was the last British Governor of Hong Kong?

4 What year did China regain Hong Kong?

5 Which US politician asked his audience to throw waffles during his election speeches?

6 Whom did he accuse of 'waffling'?

7 Which Central American leader was convicted of drug trafficking?

8 What job did Edith Cresson lose in 1992?

9 Where was Paolo Borsellino murdered?

10 What was his job?

11 Which two countries settled a 130-year-old border dispute in 1992?

12 Which country's government sat in Seoul?

13 Where was the Khmer Rouge ordered to disarm?

14 Which African country was led by Joaquim Chissano?

15 Who called 1992 'The most unpleasant year of my life'?

ANSWERS

1, Canada 2, Germany 3, Chris Patten 4, 1997 5, Dan Quayle 6, Bill Clinton 7, Manuel Noriega 8, Prime minister of France 9, Sicily 10, Chief prosecutor in an anti-Mafia campaign 11, Honduras and El Salvador 12, South Korea's 13, Cambodia 14, Mozambique 15, George Bush

QUIZ 65

ARTS & ENTERTAINMENT

1 Who played a penniless artist aboard a doomed ship?

2 And the film he appeared in?

3 How many Academy Awards did this film win?

4 Which earlier film's Oscar haul did this achievement equal?

5 Which actress starred in the play *Amy's View?*

6 In which 'alphabetical' film role did she have to deal with 007?

7 And which queen had she played in 1997?

8 In which film?

9 Where was Europe's new Guggenheim Museum?

10 Where was the Knitting Factory jazz club?

11 Which great German composer's centenary was celebrated in 1997?

12 Was the Lilith Fair music festival a) hard rock only b) girls only c) 50s revivalists only?

13 Who made a 1997 album called 'Time Out of Mind'?

14 Who led a new Texan band, The Wallflowers?

15 In the dance-world, what did ABT signify?

ANSWERS

1, Leonardo Di Caprio 2, *Titanic* 3, 11 4, *Ben-Hur* (1959) 5, Judi Dench 6, 'M' in the Bond films 7, Queen Victoria 8, *Mrs Brown* 9, Bilbao 10, New York 11, Brahms 12, b) 13, Bob Dylan 14, Jakob Dylan (son of Bob) 15, American Ballet Theatre

QUIZ 66

CAN YOU DECIPHER THESE MILITARY ABBREVIATIONS ALL CURRENT IN THE 90S?

1 APC?

2 ATBM?

3 START?

4 MIRV?

5 SAM?

6 TBM?

7 NATO?

8 FGA?

9 ASW?

10 SLBM?

11 WEU?

12 AWACS?

13 ACC (in the USA)?

14 ICBM?

15 ALCM?

ANSWERS

1, Armoured Personnel Carrier 2, Anti-Tactical Ballistic Missile 3, Strategic Arms Reduction Treaty 4, Multiple Independently Targeted Re-entry Vehicle 5, Surface-to-Air Missile 6,Theatre Ballistic Missile 7, North Atlantic Treaty Organization 8, Fighter Ground Attack 9, Anti Submarine Warfare 10, Submarine Launched Ballistic Missile 11,Western European Union 12, Airborne Warning and Control System 13, Air Combat Command 14, Inter-Continental Ballistic Missile 15, Air-Launched Cruise Missile

QUIZ 67

ARTS & ENTERTAINMENT

1 Who starred in the film of *Evita* (as Evita)?

2 Was *Thunderheart* a) a film about a part-Indian FBI Agent or b) a meteorologist fighting alien invaders?

3 Which 1997 film reunited the lead actors from *A Fish Called Wanda?*

4 Who played Ada in *The Piano?*

5 Who starred alongside Sylvester Stallone in *Demolition Man?*

6 For which film did Gene Hackman win the 1993 best-actor award?

7 What nationality was director Michael Caccoyannis?

8 Which country produced a 1993 film of Zola's novel *Germinal?*

9 Who was the female star of *Sleepless in Seattle?*

10 Who starred in *Terminator 2?*

11 What was the film's sub-title: a) *Judgement Day* or b) *The Bad Ending?*

12 Who starred as Hannibal Lecter?

13 Name of the film?

14 And his female co-star?

15 Which of them won an Oscar?

ANSWERS

1, Madonna 2, a) 3, *Fierce Creatures* 4, Holly Hunter 5, Wesley Snipes
6, *The Unforgiven* 7, Greek 8, France 9, Meg Ryan 10, Arnold
Schwarzenegger 11, a) 12, Anthony Hopkins 13, *The Silence Of The Lambs*
14, Jodie Foster 15, They both did

QUIZ 68

SPORT

SOCCER

1 Which French team was relegated after a bribing scandal (1993-1994)?

2 Which Scottish club signed Brian Laudrup from Fiorentina?

3 Which famous British club manager died in 1994?

4 Which British club won the European Cup-Winner's Cup in 1994?

5 For whom did Marcel Desailly score the winner in the 1994 European Champion's Cup final?

6 Whom did his team beat?

7 Score?

8 Where were the 1994 World Cup finals staged?

9 Which international tournament did Denmark win in 1992?

10 Where was the tournament staged?

11 Which Welsh striker left Derby for Liverpool in 1991?

12 Which Italian club did David Platt join that year?

13 Which British club did he leave?

14 Was the fee a)£2.5 million b)£4million c)£5.5million?

15 Which national league did Cwmbran win in 1993?

ANSWERS

1, Marseille 2, Rangers 3, Sir Matt Busby 4, Arsenal 5, AC Milan 6, Barcelona 7, 4-0 8, United States 9, European Championship 10, Sweden 11, Dean Saunders 12, Bari 13, Aston Villa 14, c) 15, Welsh

QUIZ 69

POT LUCK

1 What did Louise Greenfarb have 17,000 examples of in 1996?

2 Which actor, who died in 1999, played General Patton on screen?

3 Which city changed its name to Kolkata in July 1999?

4 Which country's population topped the 1 billion mark in 1999?

5 What was cooked in Rotherham in August 1991 to celebrate Yorkshire Day?

6 What super-tall structure fell down in Poland in 1991?

7 Which British actress appeared on TV in 1991 aged 100?

8 Complete the 1993 movie title: *The Long Kiss*-------?

9 Which 11-year-old starred in *My Girl* (1991)?

10 Which world title did Larry Kahn of the USA win for the 14th time in 1995?

11 Which two UK drugs companies were involved in a 1995 takeover struggle?

12 Which British peer left 130 million in his 1994 will?

13 Which country had the world's biggest army in 1995?

14 What nationality was 90s athlete Nouredine Morceli?

15 Who scored England's second goal against Scotland in the Euro 96 soccer match at Wembley?

ANSWERS

1, Fridge magnets 2, George C. Scott 3, Calcutta 4, India's 5, A giant Yorkshire Pudding 6, The Warsaw Radio mast 7, Gwen Ffrancon-Davies 8, *Goodnight* 9, Macaulay Culkin 10, Tiddlywinks 11, Glaxo and Wellcome 12, The Marquess of Bute 13, China 14, Algerian 15, Paul Gascoigne

QUIZ 70

ARTS & ENTERTAINMENT

Can you complete these hit titles?

1 'Nothing Compares---------'?
2 'Dirty---------'?
3 'I Still Haven't Found------'?
4 'November Spawned-------'?
5 'Papa Was A ----------------'?-
6 'Hanky---------------'?
7 'Thunderbirds---------'?
8 'Itsy Bitsy ------------'?
9 'Naked in the -----'?
10 'Unchained----------'?
11 'Groove Is In -------'?
12 'Kinky-----------'?
13 'Mary Had A------'?
14 'Blue---------'?
15 'Tears On My------'?

ANSWERS

1, 2 U 2, Cash 3, What I'm Looking For 4, A Monster 5, Rolling Stone
6, Panky 7, Are Go 8, Teeny Weeny Yellow Polka Dot Bikini 9, Rain
10, Melody 11, The Heart 12, Boots 13, Little Boy 14, Velvet 15, Pillow

QUIZ 71

SCIENCE & TECHNOLOGY

1 With what controversial issue was Dr Jack Kevorkian linked?

2 Eating this was found to increase the risk of prostate cancer: what?

3 Which bird was found to mimic other wild birds, as well as human speech?

4 Where was a new animal, described as the 'forest goat' discovered?

5 Where was the new TGV Nord line opened?

6 Which country launched Progress spacecraft?

7 Which Antarctic volcano was explored by robot in 1993?

8 Can you name the robot?

9 Did it have wheels or legs?

10 What was the aim of this experiment?

11 What happened to the Landsat 6 satellite?

12 Which woman became Australia's new minister of health in 1994?

13 Was Alonzo Church (died 1993) a mathematician, astronaut or heart surgeon?

14 What museum opened its Enola Gay exhibit in 1995?

15 What was the centrepiece of the exhibit?

ANSWERS

1, Euthanasia 2, Red meat 3, Grey Parrot 4, Vietnam 5, France 6, Russia 7, Erebus 8, Dante 9, Legs (8) 10, To test planetary explorers 11, It blew up shortly after launch in 1993 12, Carmen Lawrence 13, Mathematician 14, The Smithsonian Institution, Washington 15, The B-29 bomber that dropped the Hiroshima A-bomb

PEOPLE

ABOUT PEOPLE WHO DIED IN 1998

1 Who was 'Battling Bella' in the USA?

2 Which two singing cowboys rode into the sunset in 1998?

3 Which one of them rode a horse called Trigger?

4 Of what duo was Salvatore Bono once half?

5 In what art form did Christopher Gable perform?

6 What game did Justin Fashanu play?

7 Which American politician noted for his right-wing views died this year?

8 Who had beaten him in the 1964 presidential election?

9 What was Linda McCartney's name before her marriage?

10 Which industry had Sir Ian MacGregor headed in the 1980s?

11 Who was Jerome Robbins?

12 He'd been the first American in space: who was he?

13 'The Voice'?

14 The most famous child expert of his day?

15 And the 100-film actor, who starred as Marcus Welby MD on TV in the 1970s?

ANSWERS

1, Lawyer and politician Bella Abzug 2, Roy Rogers and Gene Autry 3, Roy Rogers 4, Sonny and Cher 5, Ballet 6, Soccer 7, Barry Goldwater 8, Lyndon Johnson 9, Eastman 10, The National Coal Board 11, An American choreographer 12, Alan Shepard Jr 13, Frank Sinatra 14, Dr Benjamin Spock 15, Robert Young

QUIZ 73

ARTS & ENTERTAINMENT

1 Who sang 'But Seriously'?

2 Whose 7 hits in the year (1990) equalled a 1956 record?

3 Who set the record?

4 Which ex-Avengers stars hit the charts in 1990?

5 Who sang 'Without You' in 1994?

6 Which 60s hit song was re-recorded by Chaka Demus and the Pliers in 1994?

7 Which artist recorded 'Belissima' in 1997?

8 Which group hit the 96 chart with 'Wannabe'?

9 From which film did the hit 'Born Slippy' come?

10 Who had a hit with this track?

11 Which '92 group recorded 'Deeply Dippy'?

12 Which US singer made the 'Human Touch' album?

13 Guns N' – what?

14 Who recorded the tribute song 'Abba-Esque'?

15 Who was 'in the closet' in 1992?

ANSWERS

1, Phil Collins 2, New Kids On The Block 3, Bill Haley and The Comets 4, Honor Blackman and Patrick MacNee 5, Mariah Carey 6, Twist and Shout 7, DJ Quicksilver 8, The Spice Girls 9, *Trainspotting* 10, Underworld 11, Right Said Fred 12, Bruce Springsteen 13, Roses 14, Erasure 15, Michael Jackson ('In The Closet')

QUIZ 74

POT LUCK

1 Complete the TV title: *Murder, She* -----?

2 Who starred in *Prime Suspect 3?*

3 Which country launched the Geotail satellite?

4 What nationality was GP driver Roland Ratzenberger?

5 At which race track was he killed in 1994?

6 What do the initials GATT stand for?

7 In which business did Abode and Aldus merge: a) software b) fashion c) housebuilding?

8 Which plant-crop was hit by disease in India and China in the mid-90s: a) rice b) silk c) cotton?

9 Which sea saw the worst-ever ferry disaster (1994)?

10 Which country's art featured in a US exhibition called 'Treasures from Heaven'?

11 Which fish was caught in the greatest tonnage in the early 90s: a) cod b) anchoveta c) herring?

12 In which sport did Jean Borotra become famous?

13 What year did he die, aged 95?

14 Who played the author in the film *Shadowlands?*

15 And who was the real-life author portrayed in the film?

ANSWERS

1, *Wrote* 2, Helen Mirren 3, Japan 4, Austrian 5, San Marino 6, General Agreement on Tariffs and Trade 7, a) 8, c) 9, Baltic 10, Armenia 11, b) 12, Tennis 13, 1994 14, Anthony Hopkins 15, C S Lewis

QUIZ 75

ARTS & ENTERTAINMENT

1 In which 1992 film did a cheerleader take on the bloodsuckers?

2 Which industry was uncovered in the 1995 documentary *Unzipped?*

3 What sport was featured in the 1993 Disney film *Cool Runnings?*

4 Was there really a 1993 film called *Groundhog Day?*

5 Which 1992 film secured an Oscar for Emma Thompson as best actress?

6 Who wrote the novel from which the film was adapted?

7 Who directed *The Silence of the Lambs?*

8 Both stars of this film won Oscars: who was the actress?

9 And who was the actor?

10 Complete the Al Pacino film title: *Scent of a* ------?

11 In which film did Kathy Bates win an Oscar?

12 Was *Unforgiven* a) a Western b) a horror film c) a romantic comedy?

13 Which veteran bad-guy actor starred in *City Slickers?*

14 Which actor pursued runaway Harrison Ford in a 1993 thriller?

15 And the film title?

ANSWERS

1, *Buffy the Vampire Slayer* 2, The fashion industry 3, Bobsledding 4, Yes
5, *Howards End* 6, E M Forster 7, Jonathan Demme 8, Jodie Foster
9, Anthony Hopkins 10, *Woman* 11, *Misery* 12, c) 13, Jack Palance
14, Tommy Lee Jones 15, *The Fugitive*

QUIZ 76

SPORT

1 What kind of craft was a Wills Wing?

2 In which sport was the 'sequential jumping' event of 1990 won by France?

3 Can you name these two French racing drivers: Alain------?

4 Jean------?

5 Which motor race did Arie Luyendyk win in 1990?

6 In what game did Pittsburgh's Penguins excel?

7 In which sport did New Zealand win the 1991 Coronation Cup?

8 Was Miss Budweiser a) a beauty queen b) a horse c) a motorboat?

9 Who won the 1992 Wimbledon men's singles?

10 Whom did he beat in the final?

11 In which sport was Paul Acola of Switzerland a 90s star?

12 From which sport did Susan Devoy retire in 1992?

13 Was William Sigei good at cross-country, judo or chess?

14 Which Sonia ran for Ireland?

15 Which soccer team did the double (league and Cup) in 1994?

ANSWERS

1, A hang glider 2, Parachuting 3, Prost 4, Alesi 5, Indianapolis 500 6, Ice Hockey 7, Polo 8, c) 9, Andre Agassi 10, Goran Ivanisevic 11, Skiing 12, Squash 13, Cross-country 14, Sonia O'Sullivan 15, Manchester United

ARTS & ENTERTAINMENT

1 Who took *Believe* to a 1998 number one?

2 Who had a hit with *Viva Forever?*

3 How old was Billie when she had her first chart-topper?

4 Who were back in the charts with an old *Grease* favourite?

5 Complete the title: *Sex On The* -------?

6 Which Spice Girl said goodbye?

7 Who asked 'let me entertain you'?

8 Who was 'ol' Blue Eyes'?

9 Complete the band name: The Squirrel----- -----?

10 Who was 'frozen'?

11 *Never Ever* was a hit for -------- who?

12 Who sang *My Heart Will Go On?*

13 Who recorded *Cleopatra's Theme?*

14 Who made the charts with *Everlasting Love?*

15 Who entered the Top 20 with *Dreams?*

ANSWERS

1, Cher 2, The Spice Girls 3, 16 4, John Travolta and Olivia Newton-John 5, *Beach* 6, Ginger (Geri Halliwell) 7, Robbie Williams 8, Frank Sinatra 9, Nut Zippers 10, Madonna 11, All Saints 12, Celine Dion 13, Cleopatra 14, Cast from Casualty 15, Corrs

QUIZ 78

PEOPLE

1 Who was 'Australia's chief emissary of culture'?

2 And who portrayed him on stage and TV?

3 What nationality is film-maker Ang Lee?

4 Who was Tara Lipinski?

5 At which Olympics did she strike gold?

6 And whose 70-year-old record did she break?

7 In what sport did Pak Se Ri make her name?

8 Who staged a 40th-anniversary fashion show in the Stade de France?

9 In which movie did Lian Neeson wield a light-sabre?

10 Complete the celebrity name: Puff-----?

11 Where did Putin hold the reins of power?

12 Who played talk-show host Larry Sanders?

13 Which prime minister's wife announced in 1999 she was pregnant?

14 Who scored two goals for France in the 1998 World Cup final?

15 Dubbed 'Britain's queen of the blues' she died in 1998: who was she?

ANSWERS

1, Sir Les Patterson 2, Barry Humphries 3, Taiwanese 4, An American skater 5, 1998 6, Sonja Henie's (youngest skating gold medallist 7, Women's golf 8, Yves Saint Laurent 9, *Star Wars: Episode One The Phantom Menace* 10, Puff Daddy 11, Russia 12, Gary Shandling 13, Tony Blair's wife Cherie 14, Zinedine Zidane 15, Beryl Bryden

QUIZ 79

SCIENCE & TECHNOLOGY

1 What unusual fossils were found 250 miles from the South Pole in 1991?

2 Which British university was 20 years old in 1991?

3 What did the initials UNCED stand for?

4 Which Californian vulture was being rescued from extinction?

5 Which man-made disaster put 1000 times as much soot as normal into the air?

6 What was the DCS 460 introduced by Eastman Kodak in 1994?

7 What was the Power PC 620?

8 Which Portuguese river was spanned by a new bridge?

9 Which Chicago building lost its tallest-yet spot?

10 Which European country led the way in unleaded fuel sales in the early 90s?

11 Which island was hit by 'the cyclone of the century' in 1994?

12 Where was a 5000-year-old frozen corpse discovered?

13 WHO declared war on smoking. Who is WHO?

14 Was Brent Blend: a) a cigarette b) a kind of crude oil c) a new teabag?

15 Which pipsqueak computer was 10 years old in 1994?

ANSWERS

1, Beech tree leaves 2, The Open University 3, United Nations Conference on Environment and Development 4, The California condor 5, The burning of Kuwait's oil wells 6, A digital camera 7, A 64-bit microprocessor 8, The Tagus 9, The Sears Tower 10, Germany 11, Madagascar 12, In the Alps 13, The World Health Organisation 14, b) 15, The Apple Macintosh

QUIZ 80

ARTS & ENTERTAINMENT

1 Which 1990 film showed a child fending off would-be burglars?

2 Which 1991 film spoofed daytime TV serials?

3 Complete the title: *Thelma and* ------?

4 Which rescue service featured in *Backdraft?*

5 Who directed *The Fisher King?*

6 Which pop star was the focus of *Truth or Dare?*

7 Which director made a film about 60s group *The Doors?*

8 Which US president featured in a 1991 film by the same director?

9 Which singer starred in *The Prince of Tides?*

10 What number suffixed the last *Star Trek* movie?

11 And the sub-title?

12 Best picture of 1991 was *Dances with*------ what?

13 Who starred and directed?

14 In which film did Whoopi Goldberg win a best supporting actress award?

15 Who played Prospero in *Prospero's Books?*

ANSWERS

1, *Home Alone* 2, *Soapdish* 3, *Louise* 4, Firefighters 5, Terry Gilliam
6, Madonna 7, Oliver Stone 8, Kennedy in JFK 9, Barbra Streisand
10, VI (six) 11, *The Undiscovered Country* 12, *Wolves* 13, Kevin Costner
14, *Ghost* 15, John Gielgud

QUIZ 81

PEOPLE

UK POLITICIANS

1 What name did Clinton and Hague have in common (apart from William)?

2 What was William Hague's first Cabinet post (1995)?

3 Whom did Hague succeed as Tory leader?

4 What post did Geoff Hoon occupy in 1999?

5 Who was MP for Sedgefield?

6 What body did Baroness Jay lead?

7 What new post had Ron Davies aspired to in 1998?

8 Who eventually got it, but later lost it?

9 Who left the UK government over the matter of a secret house-loan?

10 Which fellow-minister was alleged to have lent him the money?

11 Which Tory leadership candidate lost his seat in 1997?

12 Who was chosen to lead the Liberal Democrats in 1999?

13 Which financier founded the Referendum Party?

14 Who became the UK's first blind Cabinet minister?

15 And for what was he responsible?

ANSWERS

1, Jefferson (their middle name) 2, Welsh Secretary 3, John Major 4, Defence Secretary 5, Tony Blair 6, The House of Lords 7, First Secretary of the Welsh Assembly 8, Alun Michael 9, Peter Mandelson 10, Geoffrey Robinson 11, Michael Portillo 12, Charles Kennedy 13, Sir James Goldsmith 14, David Blunkett 15, Education and Employment

QUIZ 82

POT LUCK

1 Which city featured in the film *The Commitments?*

2 Which country is reckoned to have the biggest Kurdish population in 1991: a) Iraq b) Turkey c) USSR?

3 Which country had the biggest fleet of merchant ships in 1990?

4 Which sport staged its sixth world championship at Perth, Australia in 1991?

5 Which South African won the 1991 Nobel Prize for Literature?

6 Of which country was Sultan Azian Shah ruler?

7 Which British royal made her first visit to Pakistan in 1991?

8 In which country was the BJP active?

9 Was the British Army's Challenger a tank, a gun, or a missile?

10 Which western lakes were invaded by mussels from Asia?

11 Can you name the mussel-pest?

12 Was Robert Venturi famous as an architect, scientist or entertainer?

13 Who was called the 'butcher of Lyon' (he died 1991)?

14 Where did King Letsie III start his reign in 1990?

15 Which orchestra replaced Solti with Barenboim in 1991?

ANSWERS

1, Dublin 2, b) 3, Liberia 4, Swimming 5, Nadine Gordimer 6, Malaysia 7, Princess Diana 8, India 9, A tank 10, The Great Lakes 11, The Caspian zebra mussel 12, Architect 13, Klaus Barbie 14, Lesotho 15, Chicago Symphony

QUIZ 83

SPORT

HORSE RACING

1 Who returned to the saddle in 1990 after five years?

2 Which classic race did Quest For Fame win that year?

3 What colour was Desert Orchid?

4 Who won the 1990 Grand National?

5 In which race did Kingston Rule set a course record in 1990?

6 In which country did Strike The Gold win a Derby in 1991?

7 Was Paul Cole a succesful 90s trainer, jockey or horse?

8 Who rode Rodrigo de Triano to victory in the 1992 2000 Guineas?

9 In which country was Pat Day a major race-winner?

10 Which horse won the 1994 Derby?

11 How many of the 36 runners finished the 1994 Grand National?

12 In which year was the Grand National declared void?

13 Why?

14 To which country were both 1992 and 1993 English Derby winners sold?

15 In which country did Andre Fabre train?

ANSWERS

1, Lester Piggott 2, The Derby 3, Grey 4, Mr Frisk 5, Melbourne Cup
6, USA, Kentucky Derby 7, Trainer 8, Lester Piggott 9, USA 10, Erhaab
11, Six 12, 1993 13, There were two false starts 14, Japan 15, France

QUIZ 84

ARTS & ENTERTAINMENT

1 Which Bob presented *The Big Match?*

2 Which Des moved over to join him?

3 Which Jerry hosted a US talk show?

4 Which chef was naked?

5 Who presented *Ready, Steady, Cook?*

6 Gaby, daughter of Terry?

7 The *Midsomer* ----- what?

8 Starring actor John------ who?

9 In which US city was *ER* set?

10 *Bodger and* ----- who (kids' TV)?

11 *Oggy and the* ------ what (more kids' TV)?

12 Still introducing snooker on TV, David V------?

13 Comedian behind Kevin the teenager?

14 Phil and Ricky from ------ which soap?

15 Nick ------ from *They Think It's All Over?*

ANSWERS

1, Bob Wilson 2, Des Lynam 3, Springer 4, Jamie Oliver 5, Fern Britton 6, Yorath 7, *Murders* 8, Nettles 9, Chicago 10, *Badger* 11, *Cockroaches* 12, Vine 13, Harry Enfield 14, *EastEnders* 15, Hancock

QUIZ 85

PEOPLE

1 With which band did Axl Rose and Slash play?

2 Whose first name was translated as 'he who confronts' (and he did)?

3 What was Phyllis Dorothy James White famous for?

4 Which actor knighted in 1991 campaigned for gays?

5 Which British Chancellor was born in Lerwick in 1942?

6 What was Kurt Masur's profession?

7 Where did Audrey McLaughlin lead the New Democratic Party?

8 Who became Ireland's first female president in 1990?

9 To which famous novel did Alexandra Ripley write a sequel?

10 What was its title?

11 Where was Monica Seles born (country)?

12 What 'youngest-ever' feat did she achieve in March 1991?

13 Which Labour leader represented Monklands East?

14 What post did he hold before becoming leader?

15 Whose 27th play, *Lost in Yonkers* opened in New York (1991)?

ANSWERS

1, Guns N' Roses 2, Saddam Hussein 3, Writing detective stories, as P D James 4, Sir Ian McKellen 5, Norman Lamont 6, Orchestral conductor 7, Canada 8, Mary Robinson 9, *Gone With The Wind* 10, *Scarlett* 11, Yugoslavia 12, Youngest-ever No 1 in tennis (17 yrs 3 months) 13, John Smith 14, Shadow Chancellor 15, Neil Simon

QUIZ 86

ARTS & ENTERTAINMENT

1 Complete the TV show title: *Blind* -------?
2 And the presenter?
3 In which TV soap did Deidre become Mrs Rashid?
4 In which TV show did Maddy string along with Jonathan?
5 Which 90s TV show was hosted by Hugh Scully?
6 Who presented the game show *Strike It Rich?*
7 Who hosted *Have I Got News For You?*
8 In which sitcom did he partner Richard Wilson?
9 What was the name of Wilson's character?
10 Which Dimbleby presented *Question Time?*
11 In which children's series did Timmy the dog appear?
12 Who succeeded David Coleman in the chair for *A Question of Sport?*
13 Which Michael read the BBC news and also presented *999?*
14 Which Carol juggled numbers on *Countdown?*
15 Which Trevor joined Alan for *Match of the Day?*

ANSWERS

1, *Date* 2, Cilla Black 3, *Coronation Street* 4, *Jonathan Creek* 5, *The Antiques Roadshow* 6, Michael Barrymore 7, Angus Deayton 8, *One Foot In The Grave* 9, Victor Meldrew 10, David 11, *The Famous Five* 12, Sue Barker 13, Michael Buerk 14, Carol Vorderman 15, Trevor Brooking

QUIZ 87

SCIENCE & TECHNOLOGY

1 Where was a royal mausoleum found in the Valley of the Kings in 1995?

2 Which country tested a nuclear device in the South Pacific that year?

3 Which telecommunications giant announced it was splitting into three?

4 With whom did the Turner Broadcasting System agree to merge?

5 Where was the Konkan rail link being built?

6 In which city was the Oriental Pearl Television Tower completed?

7 Which London Underground line was being extended eastward?

8 In which field of science was the Irish physicist Ernest Walton (died 1995) distinguished?

9 What was 1995 S4?

10 Which US spacecraft docked for the first time with a Soviet one?

11 What odd damage delayed the 1995 launch of a US spaceflight: a) rust b) ice c) woodpeckers?

12 Explain your answer!

13 How many plant and animal species are there, according to a 1995 UN estimate?

14 How many of these are identified?

15 What rare primate was under threat in Rwanda?

ANSWERS

1, Egypt 2, France 3, AT&T 4, Time Warner 5, India (Bombay-Bangalore) 6, Shanghai 7, The Jubilee line 8, Nuclear physics 9, A new moon of Saturn 10, The Shuttle 11, c) 12, The birds bored holes in fuel tank insulation 13, 15 million 14, 1.75 million 15, Mountain gorilla

QUIZ 88

PEOPLE

1 Which boss of Wimbledon FC had to retire temporarily after a heart attack in 1999?

2 What did Jan Ullrich of Germany win in 1997?

3 Which campaign did Judy Williams help found?

4 In which sport was David Graveney involved in picking a team?

5 Which BBC TV show did Jeremy Paxman host late-evening?

6 And which college quiz did he also host?

7 Who was Merrill Ashley?

8 Which airline did Bob Ayling head?

9 Which political party did Menzies Campbell represent in the UK Parliament?

10 And which new assembly did Donald Dewar become chief minister in?

11 Which party did he lead there?

12 What was Giorgio Armani's business?

13 Who starred in *Liar Liar* (1997)

14 And what was his profession in this film?

15 For what musical style was Cuba's Celia Cruz famous?

ANSWERS

1, Joe Kinnear 2, The Tour de France cycle race 3, The International Campaign to Ban Landmines 4, Cricket 5, *Newsnight* 6, *University Challenge* 7, An American ballet star 8, British Airways 9, The Liberal Democrats 10, The Scottish Assembly 11, Labour 12, Fashion 13, Jim Carrey 14, He played a lawyer 15, Salsa

QUIZ 89

ARTS & ENTERTAINMENT

1 Which fictional rabbit was 100 years old in 1993?

2 Which author created him/her?

3 Who wrote the novel *A Suitable Boy?*

4 In which field is Michael Tilson Thomas distinguished?

5 To which city did he move in 1995?

6 How many Maniacs were there (a band)?

7 How many members had Nirvana in the early 90s?

8 Who wrote the novel *The Robber Bride?*

9 Is this writer American, Australian or Canadian?

10 Who won the 1993 Nobel Peace Prize for Literature?

11 Nationality?

12 Which British architect was honoured with the highest US architectural award in 1993?

13 Whose letters to a queen went on sale in that year?

14 Who was the queen?

15 Who wrote the music for the show *Sunset Boulevard?*

ANSWERS

1, Peter Rabbit 2, Beatrix Potter 3, Vikram Seth 4, Conducting 5, San Francisco 6, 10,000 7, Three 8, Margaret Attwood 9, Canadian 10, Toni Morrison 11, American 12, Norman Foster 13, The Earl of Essex 14, Elizabeth I 15, Andrew Lloyd Webber

QUIZ 90

THEY ALL DIED IN 1997, WHAT WERE THEY FAMOUS FOR?

1 John Akii-Bua?
2 Ivor Allchurch?
3 William S Burroughs?
4 Brian Keith?
5 Helen Hull Jacobs?
6 Joyce Wethered?
7 Wilf Wooller?
8 Fred Zinnemann?
9 Elspeth Huxley?
10 Michael Hutchence?
11 Neville Crump?
12 John Denver?
13 Denis Compton?
14 Roy Lichtenstein?
15 Clyde Tombaugh?

ANSWERS

1, Ugandan athlete, 1972 gold medallist in 400m hurdles 2, Welsh footballer 3, American writer 4, American actor 5, American tennis player 6, British golfer 7, Welsh rugby player and cricketer 8, American film director 9, British writer 10, Australian rock star 11, British racehorse trainer 12, American singer 13, English cricketer 14, American artist 15, American astronomer

QUIZ 91

WORLD EVENTS

1 Which Scot became the new boss of NATO?

2 Where, what or who is Nabulus?

3 Whom did the Queen urge to divorce in 1995?

4 Which air force lost its commander-in-chief in a crash near Isfahan?

5 Which country elected President Pastrana in 1998?

6 Which country did Suni Abacha take over in 1993?

7 Which nation turned the G-7 into the G-8?

8 Where was the newly built second-largest US government building?

9 After whom was it named?

10 For what was the Templeton Prize awarded?

11 In which country was Bujumbura Airport?

12 Where did prime minister Konstantinos Simitis hold power?

13 Which country's capital was Riga?

14 Where was Harald V King?

15 Ljubljana was the new capital of-----where?

ANSWERS

1, George Robertson 2, It's the largest city in the West Bank (Palestine)
3, Prince Charles and Princess Diana 4, Iran's 5, Colombia 6, Nigeria
7, Russia 8, Washington, D.C. 9, Ronald Reagan 10, 'Progress in Religion'
11, Burundi 12, Greece 13, Latvia 14, Norway 15, Slovenia

QUIZ 92

POT LUCK

1 Which European nation dominated international basketball in 1990?

2 Who beat Mike Tyson in ten rounds?

3 Which country was also known as Myanmar?

4 What aircraft was the star of the film *Memphis Belle?*

5 Which London gangsters' career was chronicled on film?

6 Who was chairman of the US Joint Chiefs of Staff?

7 In which continent was the black-faced lion tamarin discovered?

8 And what kind of creature was it?

9 Was Rifat Ozbeck a fashion designer or politician?

10 Which Yorkshire city had a new stadium for the 1991 World Student Games?

11 In which country were 300 killed in a January 1990 train crash?

12 Which Stefan was a winner at Wimbledon?

13 Which actress wrote *Postcards from the Edge?*

14 Who starred as Dick Tracy on screen?

15 Which computer company became a billion-dollar-a-year business in 1990?

ANSWERS

1, Yugoslavia 2, James 'Buster' Douglas 3, Burma 4, A WW2 B-17 bomber
5, The Krays 6, General Colin Powell 7, South America 8, A monkey
9, A fashion designer 10, Sheffield 11, Pakistan 12, Stefan Edberg
13, Carrie Fisher 14, Warren Beatty 15, Microsoft

QUIZ 93

PEOPLE

1. Which Nobel Prize did Amartya Sen win (1998)?
2. Was Erykah Badu a) a singer b) a politician or c) a new town in Israel?
3. Who became Britain's Chancellor of the Exchequer in 1997?
4. Why was James Cameron famous?
5. Who was Matthew Bourne?
6. What novelty did he introduce to a stage classic?
7. Against whom did Paula Jones bring a famous lawsuit?
8. What nationality was Wim Duisenberg?
9. Was he a) a soccer star or b) a banker?
10. What did Georg Hackl do on ice?
11. Was Richard Holbrooke a diplomat, and architect or a cricketer?
12. Which industrial group was led and founded by Kim Woo Chong?
13. In which country was Gloria Estefan born?
14. Which 90s billionaire had begun at the age of 14 with a business called Traf-O-Data?
15. Which black actress won an Oscar for her role in *Ghost?*

ANSWERS

1, Economics 2, a) 3, Gordon Brown 4, He directed the film *Titanic* 5, A choreographer 6, His *Swan Lake* was danced by men 7, President Clinton 8, Dutch 9, b) 10, Slid on it (on a luge, or toboggan) 11, US diplomat 12, Daewoo 13, Cuba 14, Bill Gates 15, Whoopi Goldberg

QUIZ 94

SPORT

1990 WORLD CUP

1 Who won the final?

2 Whom did they beat?

3 Score?

4 Who scored the winner?

5 What was Pedro Monzon's historic achievement in the final?

6 Who coached the winning side?

7 Was the 1990 win this country's first?

8 Where did the host nation finish?

9 Where did the English team finish?

10 Who beat them in the semi-finals?

11 Which West African team impressed in the 1990 tournament?

12 Which English player cried?

13 Who was England's manager?

14 Was it the highest or lowest-scoring World Cup in history?

15 How many goals were scored: a)75 b)115 c)172?

ANSWERS

1, West Germany 2, Argentina 3, 1-0 4, Andreas Brehme 5, First player to be sent off in a World Cup final 6, Franz Beckenbauer 7, No, their third 8, Third 9, Fourth 10, West Germany 11, Cameroon 12, Paul Gascoigne 13, Bobby Robson 14, Lowest 15, b)115

QUIZ 95

PEOPLE

1 In which sport did Hawaiian-born Chadwick Rowan become famous as 'Akebono'?

2 What was the name of Belgian King Albert's wife?

3 Where was General Aydid on the UN wanted list?

4 Whose first names are Anthony Charles Lynton?

5 In which country was Edouard Balladur a politician?

6 Which duo starred in the film *Dead Again* (1991)?

7 By what name was Avril Phaedra Campbell better known?

8 What job did she hold for less than 5 months?

9 Who headed a US Task Force in National Health Care Reform?

10 Who was born William Jefferson Blythe IV?

11 Who became UK Home Secretary in April 1992?

12 What job did he move to in May 1993?

13 Where was Hamar Franco made president in 1993?

14 In what sport was Chip Hanaver a US star?

15 Who wrote *The Pelican Brief*?

ANSWERS

1, Sumo wrestling 2, Queen Paola 3, Somalia 4, Tony Blair 5, France 6, Kenneth Branagh and Emma Thompson 7, Kim Campbell 8, Prime minister of Canada (1993) 9, Hillary Clinton 10, Bill Clinton 11, Kenneth Clarke 12, Chancellor of the Exchequer 13, Brazil 14, Powerboat racing 15, John Grisham

QUIZ 96

HITS OF 1997

1 *Un-break My----?*

2 *Say ---- ----- ----?*

3 *Encore ----- -----?*

4 *I Believe ---- ---- ----?*

5 *Old Before ---- -----?*

6 *Blood On The ----- -----?*

7 *I'll Be ----- -----?*

8 *California ------?*

9 *Mo Money ---- -----?*

10 *Barbie ---?*

11 *Teletubbies Say ---- -----?*

12 *Spice Up Your ------?*

13 *Bitter Sweet -----?*

14 *In My ------?*

15 *I Can Make You----- ------?*

ANSWERS

1, Heart 2, What You Want 2, Une Fois 4, I Can Fly 5, I Die 6, Dance Floor 7, Missing You 8, Dreamin 9, Mo Problems 10, Girl 11, Eh-Oh! 12, Life 13, Symphony 14, Bed 15, Feel Good

QUIZ 97

WORLD EVENTS

1 Which two leaders signed the START II treaty?

2 Was it: a) a missile reduction treaty b) a trade treaty c) an environmental treaty?

3 Which Kenyan leader became president for the 4th time?

4 Which country was led by Taisoeach Reynolds?

5 Whose Crown Prince became engaged in January 1993?

6 Who was sworn in as 42nd President?

7 And who quit as Canada's prime minister?

8 Which city in the USA was hit by a terrorist bomb attack in February?

9 Who was chosen to be China's new president?

10 Where was Percival Patterson prime minister?

11 Which new nation joined the UN in April?

12 Its flag was a sun-disk, a symbol of which ancient ruler?

13 Which Texan town was the scene of a religious-cult tragedy?

14 Which sect was involved?

15 What happened to the cult's HQ?

ANSWERS

1, Pres. Bush and Pres. Yeltsin 2, a) 3, Daniel arap Moi 4, Ireland 5, Japan's
6, Bill Clinton 7, Brian Mulroney 8, New York City 9, Jang Zemin
10, Jamaica 11, Macedonia 12, Alexander the Great 13, Waco
14, The Branch Davidians 15, It was attacked by US federal agents and
burned down

QUIZ 98

HITS OF 1994

1 Who sang about her 'hero'?

2 The *Power of Love* was a US number one for----?

3 Which reggae band hit the top with *Oh Carolina?*

4 Which band took *Everything Changes* into the charts?

5 One of the band was named Songwriter of the Year in the UK. Who?

6 What did TAFKAP represent?

7 Which band recorded *Love Is All Around?*

8 Ace of Base had a big spring '94 hit with ----- what?

9 *I Swear* was a hit for ------ who?

10 Who were singing *Come On You Reds?*

11 Who was on the streets of Philadelphia, in song?

12 Who wanted us to meet 'the swamp thing'?

13 *Regulate* was a 94 hit for Warren G and who?

14 *Stay* was a US success for L--- L--- and N--- S----. Who were they?

15 Who told us 'girls just want to have fun'?

ANSWERS

1, Mariah Carey (*Hero*) 2, Celine Dion 3, Shaggy 4, Take That 5, Gary Barlow 6, The Artist Formely Known As Prince 7, Wet Wet Wet 8, *The Sign* 9, All-4-One 10, Man Utd squad 11, Bruce Springsteen 12, Grid 13, Nate Dogg 14, Lisa Loeb and Nine Stories 15, Cyndi Lauper

QUIZ 99

PEOPLE

1 Who fell out with her boss Michael Howard?

2 Who left his Radio 1 breakfast show in 1997?

3 Who called the Queen 'the best of British'?

4 Who called an ex-pupil 'pretty full of himself'?

5 Of whom was he speaking?

6 Who called Baroness Emma Nicholson a 'mad cow'?

7 Who was called 'the worst human being on the planet'?

8 By whom?

9 Which UK politician took to wearing a baketball cap?

10 Who complained about 'these awful things on tails'?

11 Which Beatle's daughter was a rising fashion designer?

12 Which cricketer said 'the tank is empty'?

13 Which politician said 'my mind is very, very open and so is my mouth'?

14 Who was described during an England soccer match in Rome as looking 'like a pint of Guinness running around'?

15 And who said this?

ANSWERS

1, Ann Widdecombe 2, Chris Evans 3, Tony Blair 4, Eric Anderson of Fettes School 5, Ex-pupil Tony Blair 6, Winnie Mandela 7, Woody Allen 8, André Previn 9, William Hague 10, Mrs Thatcher (of BA's new airliner livery) 11, Paul McCartney's daughter Stella 12, Graham Gooch 13, Tony Blair 14, Paul Ince (head bandaged) 15, Paul Gascoigne

QUIZ 100

SPORT

1 In which sport was Gillian Clarke a star?

2 Who won the 1990 World Series in baseball?

3 What was Ayrton Senna's position in the 1990 Grand Prix world championship?

4 For whom was he driving?

5 Which world boxing title (by weight) did Evander Holyfield win?

6 Which two Soviet chess players contested the world title in 1990?

7 Who was reigning champion?

8 Was he still champion after the 1990 contest?

9 Which cricketer scored 333 against India?

10 Where?

11 Which New Zealander topped 400 Test wickets?

12 Which country hosted the 1990 World Cup finals?

13 What was Greg LeMond's sport?

14 What game did the Winnipeg Blue Bombers play?

15 Which jockey rode 209 winners in Britain in 1990?

ANSWERS

1, Badminton 2, Cincinatti Reds 3, 1st 4, McLaren-Honda
5, Heavyweight 6, Karpov and Kasparov 7, Gary Kasparov 8, Yes
9, Graham Gooch 10, Lord's 11, Richard Hadlee 12, Italy 13, Cycling
14, Canadian Football 15, Pat Eddery

QUIZ 101

POT LUCK

1 Which judge retired, saying the work was too strenuous?.

2 Which country held its first-ever free election?

3 Which Nobel prize did Jerome Friedman share?

4 Which British golfer won the US Masters?

5 Who challenged Margaret Thatcher for the Tory leadership?

6 Who was the new editor of *The Times* (March 1990)?

7 Who was Alice Munro?

8 Who said 'I do write too many books'?

9 And which detective featured in many of them?

10 For whom did Matthew Maynard play cricket?

11 Complete the pop band name: New Kids -------?

12 Who won an Oscar aged 80, as best actress?

13 What was the film?

14 Which French businessman tried to take over Adidas?

15 Which Tracey (from Slough) was a hit on US TV?

ANSWERS

1, US Justice William J Brennan 2, Mongolia 3, Physics 4, Nick Faldo 5, Michael Heseltine 6, Simon Jenkins 7, A Canadian novelist 8, Ruth Rendell 9, DCI Reg Wexford 10, Glamorgan and England 11, On the Block 12, Jessica Tandy 13, *Driving Miss Daisy* 14, Bernard Tapie 15, Tracey Ullmann

QUIZ 102

NAME THEIR JOB OR PROFESSION

1 Gianluca Vialli?

2 Clare Short?

3 Ralph Fiennes?

4 Jurgen Klinsmann?

5 Angus Fraser?

6 Jana Novotna?

7 Fern Britton?

8 Tinky Winky?

9 Liam Gallagher?

10 Nigel Rees?

11 George Carey?

12 Max Hastings?

13 Nigel Kennedy?

14 Keith Floyd?

15 Simon Raven?

ANSWERS

1, Footballer 2, Politician 3, Actor 4, Footballer 5, Cricketer 6, Tennis player 7, TV presenter 8, Teletubby 9, Pop singer 10, Radio presenter and journalist 11, Archbishop of Canterbury 12, Writer and Newspaper editor 13, Violinist 14, TV cook 15, Writer

QUIZ 103

ARTS & ENTERTAINMENT

1 What nationality was singer Ruby Turner?

2 Which Irish girl singer topped the February 1990 album chart?

3 Who recorded *Hangin' Tough?*

4 Who sang *Dear Jessie?*

5 A song by Andy Stewart reappeared in the 1990 charts. Title?

6 Who was singing *I Wish It Would Rain Down?*

7 Complete the 1990 song title: *How Am I Supposed To* ---------?

8 And the singer?

9 Whose *Love Shack* was in the 1990 charts?

10 *Another Day* ------. Where?

11 Cher sang *Just Like* ---------. Who?

12 What did Seduction, Expose and The Cover Girls have in common?

13 Which Gloria sang *Here We Are?*

14 Whose recording of *Strawberry Fields Forever* hit the UK Top Ten in 1990?

15 And who was on the *Downtown Train?*

ANSWERS

1, British 2, Sinead O'Connor 3, New Kids On The Block 4, Madonna 5, *Donald Where's Your Troosers* 6, Phil Collins 7 *Live Without You* 8, Michael Bolton 9, B-52s 10, *In Paradise* 11, *Jesse James* 12, They were all girl groups 13, Estefan 14, Candy Flip 15, Rod Stewart

WORLD EVENTS

1 Which currency was devalued by 1000 times its '97 value as 1998 began?

2 What post did Kofi Annan hold?

3 Which government did Lionel Jospin lead?

4 Which famous statue lost its head in 1998?

5 Was the head ever found?

6 Which communist state did the Pope visit in 1998?

7 Who said 'I did not have sexual relations with that woman'?

8 And who was the woman?

9 Which country's capital is Harare?

10 Which state took control of Eastern Slavonia in 1998?

11 Who had occupied this region since 1991?

12 Off which Caribbean island were huge new oil reserves found?

13 Where was the Te Papa Tongarewa Museum opened?

14 Where was Viktor Chernomyrdin fired as prime minister?

15 And who fired him?

ANSWERS

1, The Russian rouble 2, UN Secretary-General 3, French 4, The Little Mermaid, Copenhagen 5, Yes, after two days 6, Cuba 7, President Clinton 8, Monica Lewinsky 9, Zimbabwe 10, Croatia 11, Serbia 12, Trinidad 13, Wellington, New Zealand 14, Russia 15, Boris Yeltsin

QUIZ 105

ARTS & ENTERTAINMENT

1 Who wrote the best-seller *Rising Sun*, filmed in 1993?

2 Which 1993 Spielberg film broke box-office records?

3 Which veteran British actor appeared in it?

4 Whose novel *The Firm* was filmed?

5 Which star directed *The Man Without A Face?*

6 Who played Mrs Doubtfire?

7 Who directed *Schindler's List?*

8 Who starred in it?

9 Who starred in *Carlito's Way?*

10 What country was the setting for the film *The Piano?*

11 Who directed *The Unforgiven?*

12 Who won an Oscar for *Scent of a Woman?*

13 Which Italian director died in 1993?

14 Who was the 'First Lady of the Silent Screen' who died the same year?

15 Which actor-director made the Shakespeare film *Much Ado About Nothing?*

ANSWERS

1, Michael Crichton 2, *Jurassic Park* 3, Sir Richard Attenborough 4, John Grisham 5, Mel Gibson 6, Robin Williams 7, Steven Spielberg 8, Liam Neeson 9, Al Pacino 10, New Zealand 11, Clint Eastwood 12, Al Pacino 13, Federico Fellini 14, Lilian Gish 15, Kenneth Branagh

QUIZ 106

COMPLETE THE NAMES OF THESE CELEBRITIES WHO ALL DIED IN 1991

1 Comedian Bernie---?
2 Labour MP Eric----?
3 French actor Yves---?
4 Newspaper columnist Jean---?
5 Saxophonist Stan------?
6 *Bonanza* actor Michael-----?
7 American actress Lee----?
8 Graham ---- who wrote *The End of the Affair?*
9 Bandleader Geoff-------?
10 Jailbreaker Alfie-----?
11 Actress Coral------?
12 Publisher Robert-----?
13 Bird photographer Eric------?
14 American dance pioneer Martha----?
15 Ballerina Margot-------?

ANSWERS

1,Winters 2,Heffer 3,Montand 4,Rook 5,Getz 6,Landon 7,Remick
8,Greene 9,Love 10,Hinds 11,Browne 12,Maxwell 13,Hosking
14,Graham 15,Fonteyn

QUIZ 107

SPORT

1 In which sport did Graeme Obree break records?

2 Which English batsman hit his 100th century in 1993?

3 Which cricketing country played home tests at Colombo?

4 What game did Puerto Rica's Crab Pickers play?

5 What handicap did pitcher Jim Abbot overcome?

6 Which Formula One champion turned to Indy-Car racing in 1993?

7 In which country was the Kyalami G.P. held?

8 What game was James Wattana good at?

9 Which game did Nigel Short play for a world title?

10 Which former Spurs skipper died in 1993?

11 In which World Cup finals had he played for Northern Ireland?

12 Which Sheikh had great success on the track?

13 In which sport was Ty Murray acclaimed 'the greatest of his era'?

14 Which David was still bowling a mean wood in his 60s?

15 Was Michelle Martin 1993 world champion in squash, badminton or judo?

ANSWERS

1, Cycling 2, Graham Gooch 3, Sri Lanka 4, Baseball 5, He had no right hand 6, Nigel Mansell 7, South Africa 8, Snooker 9, Chess 10, Danny Blanchflower 11, 1958 12, Sheikh Muhammad 13, Rodeo 14, Bryant 15, Squash

QUIZ 108

PEOPLE

1 Whose nephew was William Kennedy Smith?

2 Who was Bertrand Gachot?

3 What got him into trouble in London 1991?

4 Against whom did Judy Nelson file a 'galimoney' suit?

5 Which company headed by Asil Nadir got into trouble?

6 Who was Teresa Gorman?

7 Who was accused of raping a Miss Black America contestant?

8 Whose private army was known as her 'Football Club'?

9 Which title was the Marquis of Blandford due to inherit?

10 Why was he jailed in 1991?

11 Actor Ian became Sir Ian in 1991 – surname?

12 Which tycoon denied in 1991 that he had links with Israel's secret service?

13 From what post did Sir Donald Acheson retire?

14 Which best-seller novelist expressed surprise at his book being an A-level book?

15 And the book?

ANSWERS

1, Senator Edward Kennedy's 2, A French racing driver 3, A row with a taxi driver (he ended up in jail) 4, Martina Navratilova 5, Polly Peck 6, Tory MP for Billericay 7, Mike Tyson 8, Winnie Mandela 9, Duke of Marlborough 10, Driving while disqualified 11, Sir Ian McKellen 12, Robert Maxwell 13, Britain's Chief Medical Officer 14, Frederick Forsyth 15, *The Day of The Jackal*

QUIZ 109

POT LUCK

1 By what name was the community charge better known?
2 In which country was Jean Chretien a politician?
3 In which city did the Almeida Theatre attract praise?
4 Which writer's Narnia books were a hit on TV and stage?
5 In which country was Benazir Bhutto deposed in 1990?
6 What game did the Seibu Lions play?
7 Was Grete Waitz a runner, a singer, or a TV cook?
8 Which country became the Commonwealth's 50th member in 1990?
9 What did the initials PCC mean in the media world from 1991?
10 Who wrote a long poem called *Omeros?*
11 Was the T-72 a tank or an aircraft?
12 In which country was President Kaunda defeated in 1991?
13 From which sport did I.V.A. Richards retire?
14 Was Galileo a space probe, a cruise liner or a computer system?
15 What instrument did Max Jaffa (died 1991) play?

ANSWERS

1, The poll tax 2, Canada 3, London 4, C.S. Lewis 5, Pakistan 6, Baseball (in Japan) 7, A Norwegian runner 8, Namibia 9, Press Complaints Commission 10, Derek Walcott 11, A tank 12, Zambia 13, Cricket 14, A space probe 15, Violin

QUIZ 110

ARTS & ENTERTAINMENT

1 Which punk band reappeared on the 1996 tour scene?

2 What was the tour's name?

3 Who sang *Return of The Mack?*

4 Who were 'back for good' in 1995?

5 Which two TV actors recorded *Unchained Melody* that year?

6 Whose first chart topper was *Some Might Say?*

7 *Always* was a 1994 hit for who?

8 Whose *Saturday Night* made it to number one?

9 Who sang *It's All Coming Back To Me Now?*

10 Whose *Setting Sun* rose high?

11 Who partnered Bryan Adams on *I Finally Found Someone?*

12 Which film soundtrack seemed 'unsinkable' in 1996?

13 Which UK singer became 'Sir E----' in 1998?

14 The 1995 hit *One Sweet Day* featured Boyz II Men and which female singer?

15 Who recorded *Gangsta's Paradise* (1995)?

ANSWERS

1, The Sex Pistols 2, Filthy Lucre Tour 3, Mark Morrison 4, Take That 5, Robson Green and Jerome Flynn 6, Oasis 7, Bon Jovi 8, Whigfield 9, Celine Dion 10, Chemical Brothers 11, Barbra Streisand 12, *Titanic* 13, Elton John 14, Mariah Carey 15, Coolio Featuring L.V.

QUIZ 111

ALL DIED IN 1996

1 Of which radio comedy show was Michael Bentine a founder?

2 Who was George Burn's famous wife?

3 What was ever present in George Burn's mouth while performing?

4 He directed the film *Les Enfants du Paradis:* name?

5 What did Ossie Clark design?

6 The girl star of *It Happened One Night* (1934), who won an Oscar for her performance?

7 The *Daily Mirror's* best-known agony aunt?

8 The British inventor of the jet engine?

9 The singer who sang *Tiptoe Through The Tulips* in 1968?

10 (Bet you don't know his real name)?

11 Britain's most famous woman showjumper of the 1950's?

12 The owner of London's best jazz club?

13 An American astronomer who presented the 1980s TV series *Cosmos?*

14 Two-term president of France (1982-95)?

15 The original 'Christopher Robin'?

ANSWERS

1, *The Goon Show* 2, Gracie Allen 3, A cigar 4, Marcel Carné 5, Clothes
6, Claudette Colbert 7, Marjorie Proops 8, Sir Frank Whittle 9, Tiny Tim
10, Herbert Khaury 11, Pat Smythe 12, Ronnie Scott 13, Carl Sagan
14, Francois Mitterand 15, Christopher Robin Milne

QUIZ 112

WORLD EVENTS

1 Where did Hashimoto replace Murayama?

2 Where was the Guantanamo Navel Base in the news?

3 Who held the base?

4 And who sought safety there?

5 Which royal couple announced divorce plans in 1996?

6 Which country shot down two Cessna light aircraft over the Caribbean in 1996?

7 For what crime was Yigal Amir convicted?

8 Which British product did the EU ban exports of?

9 Where was President Dudayev slain?

10 In which part of Australia did a gunman kill 35 people?

11 Where were 18 Greek tourists shot outside their hotel?

12 Where did Romano Prodi become prime minister?

13 What weapons did the UN rule to be 'uncontrollable and inhumane'?

14 Where did President Demirel escape assassination?

15 Who or what was the UNHCR, anxious about former Soviet citizens?

ANSWERS

1, Japan 2, Cuba 3, The USA 4, Cuban refugees 5, Charles and Diana 6, Cuba 7, The murder of Yitzhak Rabin 8, Beef 9, Chechnya 10, Tasmania 11, Eygpt 12, Italy 13, Land mines 14, Turkey 15, The United Nations High Commissioner for Refugees

QUIZ 113

POT LUCK

1 Who was Robson Green's singing partner in 1995?

2 Which artists had had a 1990 hit with the same song?

3 And which veteran 1990s broadcaster topped the charts with it in 1955?

4 Which country had the most radio stations in the mid-90s?

5 Did it have a) 5 million b) 7 million c) 12 million?

6 Which group released the album *Stars* in 1991?

7 Which country won the 1992 Eurovision Song Contest with *Why Me?*

8 And the singer?

9 Which highest-ever buildings were designed by Cesar Peli?

10 In which continent were they?

11 To which city did the Royal Armouries move in 1996?

12 Where had much of the collection been displayed before?

13 Which country boasted the world's biggest piggery: a) USA b) China c) Romania?

14 What was unusual about Bud Badnya's 1994 record-breaking marathon run?

15 Which opera singer was applauded in Vienna for 1 hour 20 minutes in 1991?

ANSWERS

1, Jerome Flynn 2, The Righteous Brothers (*Unchained Melody*) 3, Jimmy Young 4, USA 5, c) 6, Simply Red 7, Ireland 8, Linda Martin 9, The Petronas Towers 10, Asia (Malaysia) 11, Leeds 12, The Tower of London 13, c) 14, He ran backwards 15, Placido Domingo

QUIZ 114

ARTS & ENTERTAINMENT

1 Whose 1992 debut single was *Jump?*

2 Which film sent *Bohemian Rhapsody* back into the charts in 1992?

3 Whose 50th birthday party was held in Madison Square Garden, N.Y. in 1997?

4 What year did the Spice Girls first top the US charts?

5 Col. Tom Parker died in 1997. Whose manager was he?

6 Is Ricky Martin a) Puerto Rican b) Australian?

7 Who topped the US charts in 1999 with *No Scrubs?*

8 Whose record of *C'Est La Vie* made it to the top in 1998?

9 On which record label did *Viva Forever* appear that year?

10 And who sang it?

11 In which year did Baddiel and Skinner appear in the charts with a soccer song?

12 Whose official song was it?

13 Did it make no.1?

14 Full title please?

15 And who were co-credited as artists?

ANSWERS

1, Kriss Kross 2, Wayne's World 3, David Bowie 4, 1997 5, Elvis Presley 6, a) 7, TLC 8, B*witched 9, Virgin 10, Spice Girls 11, 1996 12, England's 13, Yes, in June 14, *Three Lions On A Shirt* 15, The Lightning Seeds

QUIZ 115

SPORT

1 Which London club did a German soccer star rejoin in 1997?

2 And who was he?

3 Name the manager who asked him help end a crisis?

4 Did the move save the manager's job?

5 In which season had the German last played in British football?

6 Which Czech left Manchester United for Barcelona?

7 In which tournament had he starred and caught the eye?

8 With which northern Rugby club was Rob Andrew boss?

9 Which Scottish brothers said farewell to international rugby?

10 Which Surrey left-hander was in and out for England's cricket team?

11 And which brothers played with him, for county and country?

12 What sport did Greg and Tim play together?

13 On which country had one of them turned his back to be British?

14 What nationality was tennis player Gustavo Kuerten?

15 In which sport was Tommy Horton a successful 'senior'?

ANSWERS

1, Tottenham Hotspur 2, Jurgen Klinsmann 3, Christian Gross 4, No 5, 1994-95 6, Karel Poborsky 7, Euro 96 8, Newcastle 9, Scott and Gavin Hastings 10, Graham Thorpe 11, Adam and Ben Hollioake 12, Tennis (Rusedski, Henman) 13, Canada 14, Brazilian 15, Golf

QUIZ 116

WORLD EVENTS

1 Which Arab ruler suffered a stroke in 1995?

2 For what trade was the so-called 'Golden Triangle' notorious?

3 Was it in: a) South America b) North Africa or c) Southeast Asia?

4 Where did Jorgé Sampaio become president in 1996?

5 Which African king died in a road accident in 1996?

6 Where did peasants revolt in Chiapas state?

7 What is the UAE?

8 And how many states belong to it?

9 Where was President Najibullah overthrown in 1992?

10 Which Islamic group took power in that country?

11 What year did Slovakia become independent?

12 Where was 'Operation Restore Hope' mounted?

13 Which government sat in Pyongyang?

14 To which island did President Aristide return in 1994?

15 Who led the SDLP in Northern Ireland?

ANSWERS

1. King Fahd of Saudi Arabia 2. Drugs 3. c) 4. Portugal 5. Lesotho's King Moshoeshoe 6. Mexico 7. United Arab Emirates 8. Seven 9. Afghanistan 10. The Taliban 11. 1993 12. Somalia 13. North Korea's 14. Haiti 15. John Hume

QUIZ 117

SPORT

MOTOR RACING

1 Who were Ferrari's two drivers for the 1990 G.P. season?

2 What nationality was driver Martin Donnelly?

3 Which British driver replaced Ayrton Senna in 1994?

4 In which country was the 1994 Pacific Grand Prix held?

5 Whose national track was the Hungaroring?

6 Which Canadian driver won the G.P. there in 1997?

7 To which country did the G.P. circus return in 1992 for the first time since 1985?

8 Who won there (as he had in 1985)?

9 What is driver Irvine's first name?

10 Which British former world champion died in 1993?

11 Where was the 1993 European G.P. held in the UK?

12 What year did Damon Hill become world champion?

13 Which team did driver Irvine (qu.9) leave in 1996 to join Ferrari?

14 What nationality was the 1997 world champion?

15 Who finished second that season but was disqualified?

ANSWERS

1, Alain Prost, Nigel Mansell 2, Irish 3, David Coulthard 4, Japan
5, Hungary's 6, Jacques Villeneuve 7, South Africa 8, Nigel Mansell
9, Eddie 10, James Hunt 11, Donington Park 12, 1996 13, Jordan
14, Canadian (Villeneuve) 15, Michael Schumacher

POT LUCK

1 Which campaign won the 1997 Nobel Peace Prize?

2 Where was the Teatro Real reopened?

3 And what is it?

4 The biggest Commonwealth country (by population) celebrated 50 years of independence in 1997. What is it?

5 At which massacre site there did the Queen lay a wreath?

6 What game did Florida Marlins play?

7 Who became Irish president in 1997?

8 From which country did the soccer club Dynamo Minsk come?

9 Of what organisation was Emeka Anyaoku head?

10 Which city was said to be the most seriously polluted: a) New York b) Moscow c) Mexico City?

11 What was the NNP Treaty?

12 Which country voted in 1993 to make high-stakes gambling legal in casinos?

13 Which country was known as Aotearoa to a minority of its people?

14 With which religion was the BJP also associated?

15 And in which country was it powerful?

ANSWERS

1, International Campaign to Ban Landmines 2, Madrid 3, An opera house 4, India 5, Amritsar 6, Baseball 7, Mary McAleese 8, Belarus 9, Commonwealth Secretariat 10, c) 11, Nuclear Non-Proliferation 12, Switzerland 13, New Zealand 14, Hinduism 15, India

QUIZ 119

COMPLETE THE ARTISTS GROUP NAMES

1 UB---?

2 They Might Be ------?

3 Don Pablo's ------?

4 Happy -------?

5 Simple ---------?

6 Jive Bunny and ---------?

7 Depeche ----------?

8 Sweet -----------?

9 Righteous -------?

10 Pet ---------?

11 Vanilla -----?

12 Partners In ----?

13 Kylie -------?

14 Whitney --------?

15 Lisa --------?

ANSWERS

1, 40 2, Giants 3, Animals 4, Mondays 5, Minds 6, The Mastermixers 7, Mode 8, Sensation 9, Brothers 10, Shop Boys 11, Ice 12, Kryme 13, Minogue 14, Houston 15, Stansfield

QUIZ 120

PEOPLE

1 Which England centre-forward, who died in 1996, had been the youngest-ever England international in 1938?

2 Which double-Nobel prize winner died in 1994?

3 And which two prizes were they?

4 Max Factor died in 1996: with which business was his name associated?

5 Which party dance-song did Larry La Prise write?

6 Who was the spy at the heart of the Portland spy ring?

7 On what was Subrahmanyan Chandrasekhar and expert?

8 What did Susie Cooper design?

9 Which lawyer who died in 1995 was nicknamed 'the Establishment's fixer'?

10 He wrote comedy with Dennis Norden: who was he?

11 Which kind of motor did Eric Laithwaite pioneer?

12 His last parliamentary seat was in South Down: who was he?

13 What had Hans von Ohain seen fly in 1938?

14 Was Dame Mary Cartwright a mathematician, actress or writer?

15 Who was Galina Ulanova?

ANSWERS

1, Tommy Lawton 2, Linus Pauling 3, Chemistry and Peace 4, Cosmetics
5, The Hokey-Cokey 6, Peter Kroger 7, Astronomy, especially black holes
8, Ceramics 9, Lord Goodman 10, Frank Muir 11, Linear induction motor
12, Enoch Powell 13, His design for a jet plane 14, Mathematics
15, A Russian ballerina

QUIZ 121

WORLD EVENTS

1 Was Esko Aho a) a city b) a terrorist group or c) a politician?

2 Whose government did Yitzhak Rabin head?

3 Who welcomed the Queen in Cape Town?

4 Where did two banks plan to merge to form the world's biggest bank?

5 Which US city was hit by a bomb outrage in April 1995?

6 Where did Robert Mugabe hold on to power?

7 Of which country was Alberto Fujimori president?

8 Which guerrilla group had he combatted?

9 Which North American country was in a tangle with the EU over fish?

10 Whom did Chirac replace in May '95?

11 And in what position?

12 What was Chirac's first name?

13 Whose papers did the British government buy for £12.5 million?

14 Which island did Rauf Denktash rule (in part)?

15 Which country agreed to sell Iran 100 T-72 tanks?

ANSWERS

1, c) in Finland 2, Israel's 3, Nelson Mandela 4, Japan 5, Oklahoma City 6, Zimbabwe 7, Chile 8, Shining Path 9, Canada 10, Mitterand 11, President of France 12, Jacques 13, Winston Churchill's 14, Cyprus 15, Poland

QUIZ 122

COMPLETE THE NAMES OF THESE 90S WRITERS

1 Susan S------?
2 Alice W------?
3 Ian Mc-------?
4 Muriel S-----?
5 Malcom B----?
6 John U-------?
7 V. S. N-------?
8 Gwendolyn B----?
9 E. L. D-------?
10 Carlos F------?
11 Martin A------?
12 J. G. B--------?
13 Norman M----?
14 Stephen K-----?
15 Terry P-------?

ANSWERS

1, Sontag 2, Walker 3, McEwan 4, Spark 5, Bradbury 6, Updike 7, Naipaul
8, Brooks 9, Doctorow 10, Fuentes 11, Amis 12, Ballard 13, Mailer
14, King 15, Pratchett

QUIZ 123

POT LUCK

1 Which England footballer appeared for a French team in the 1991 European Cup Final?

2 Which team did he represent?

3 Which actress starred in the 1990 film *Not Without My Daughter?*

4 What sport did John Whitaker compete in?

5 Which famous Manchester speedway track faced an uncertain future?

6 Who became the youngest-ever Welsh soccer international in 1991?

7 Which was the world's largest retailer in the 90s?

8 In which city did the UK's largest strike end in 1994?

9 Any idea when it had begun?

10 Which country had the biggest national debt in the decade?

11 And which had the highest revenue?

12 What did Susan Williams blow to a diameter of 58cm in 1994?

13 What was the profession of veteran Russian cosmonaut Valeriy Poliyakov?

14 What was the 'Mendelssohn Stradivarius' sold in 1990?

15 Vivien Jones ended her distinguished career in 1994: what sport?

ANSWERS

1, Chris Waddle 2, Marseille 3, Sally Field 4, Show jumping 5, Belle Vue 6, Ryan Giggs 7, Wal-Mart Stores, Inc 8, Sheffield 9, 1986 10, The USA 11, The USA 12, Bubble-gum 13, Doctor 14, Violin 15, Hockey

QUIZ 124

ALL DIED IN THE 90S: WHAT DID THEY DO?

1 Fred Davis?

2 Octavio Paz?

3 Sam Cummings?

4 Adriana Caselotti?

5 John Bardeen?

6 Alan Shepard?

7 Sir Isaiah Berlin?

8 A.L. Rowse?

9 Stephane Grapelli?

10 Hughie Greene?

11 Charlie Chester?

12 Harold Robbins?

13 Freddie Brown?

14 Cavan O'Connor?

15 Hastings Banda?

ANSWERS

1, Snooker player 2, Writer 3, Arms dealer 4, Snow White's voice in the Disney classic 5, Physicist 6, Astronaut 7, Philosopher 8, Historian 9, Jazz violinist 10, TV game show host 11, Comedian 12, Novelist 13, Cricketer 14, Singer 15, Politician, leader of Malawi?

QUIZ 125

SPORT

1 In which sport was Chen Lu world champion in 1995?

2 Which French footballer was charged with assaulting an English fan?

3 Which millionaire backed Blackburn Rovers?

4 Which major golf championship did John Daly win in 1991?

5 Who were rugby Five Nations champions in 1993?

6 How heavy was Jonah Lomu (to the nearest 10 pounds)?

7 In which sport was Jansher Khan dominant in 1995?

8 Dennis Pankratov swam, boxed or rode horses?

9 What year were the last Olympics of the 90s?

10 Which Briton triple-jumped to fame?

11 Who won the Australia men's single tennis title in 1992 and 1993?

12 Who partnered Michael Stich to win the 1992 Wimbledon men's doubles?

13 Which soccer team beat Barcelona 4-0 to win the 1993-94 European Cup?

14 In which sport did Fabio Castartelli crash to his death in 1995?

15 Which of these was not a famous US racehorse: a) Holy Bull b)Holy Cow c) Cigar?

ANSWERS

1, Figure skating 2, Eric Cantona 3, Jack Walker 4, US PGA 5, France 6, 260 pounds 7, Squash 8, He was a swimmer (Russian) 9, 1996 10, Jonathan Edwards 11, Jim Courier 12, John McEnroe 13, AC Milan 14, Cycling 15, b)

QUIZ 126

PEOPLE

1 Of which group was Stig Anderson the mastermind?

2 Where did Pom Oliver and friends go to in 1997?

3 Which rock star was the first to get a blue plaque?

4 Which classical composer had a plaque next door, in Mayfair?

5 Where did Abdullah succeed Hussein?

6 By what name did Gonxha Bojaxhiu become world-famous?

7 Who were TV's Two Fat Ladies?

8 Who was Doreen Valiente: a) a circus star b) a rock singer c) a witch?

9 Whose bones did Morgherita Guarducci believe she'd found?

10 And where were they, according to this archaeologist?

11 Which group of people celebrated Kwanzaa?

12 And what was it?

13 Who became the ex-'First Lady of the Philippines'?

14 Who was the first woman to climb Everest without oxygen and alone?

15 Which former Northern Ireland minister ended the 90s as Conservative Party Chairman?

ANSWERS

1, ABBA 2, The North Pole 3, Jimi Hendrix 4, Handel 5, Jordan 6, Mother Teresa 7, Jennifer Paterson and Clarissa Dickson Wright 8, c) She died in 1999 9, St Peter's 10, Beneath the Vatican 11, Black Americans 12, A new New Year festival 13, Imelda Marcos 14, Alison Hargreaves in 1995 15, Michael Ancram

QUIZ 127

ART & ENTERTAINMENT

1 What nationality was the 1994 Nobel laureate for literature?

2 Who wrote a book called *Diana, Her New Life?*

3 Which novelist published *You Can't Do Both* (1994)?

4 In which islands was writer George Mackay Brown living?

5 Which US writer wrote the play *Three Tall Women?*

6 Which Australian wrote *Jacko, The Great Intruder?*

7 What was Michael Ondaatye's hit novel?

8 Who was described as 'a lord of the global village'?

9 Who was said to be the 'best poet laureate since Tennyson'?

10 Who made this comment?

11 And what happened to him?

12 In which European country were most books published in the 90's?

13 Which novelist wrote a biography of Jesus?

14 Which poet wrote a play called *The Odyssey?*

15 Who wrote the 1992 novel *Outerbridge Reach?*

ANSWERS

1, Japanese 2, Andrew Morton 3, Kingsley Amis 4, The Orkneys 5, Edward Albee 6, Thomas Kenneally 7, *The English Patient* 8, Rupert Murdoch 9, Ted Hughes 10, Andrew Motion 11, He succeeded Hughes as Poet Laureate 12, The UK 13, A N Wilson 14, Derek Walcott 15, Robert Stone

QUIZ 128

POT LUCK

1 Which Tom starred in *Mission: Impossible?*

2 Who was his off-screen wife?

3 Was Alek Wek a) a model b) a scientist or c) a TV presenter?

4 In which country did Maurice Papon go on trial?

5 With what was he charged?

6 Which new library was hastily fitted with shutters to keep the sun off its books?

7 In which country was the Robben Island Museum?

8 Who was its most famous former inmate?

9 Which animal was declared the only ancestor of the domestic dog?

10 Who wrote the novel *Quarantine?*

11 What nationality was Juliette Binoche?

12 And her profession?

13 Who became Britain's youngest prime minister?

14 How old was he?

15 And who was the 18th-century politician who'd made it to the top even younger?

ANSWERS

1,Tom Cruise 2,Nicole Kidman 3,a) 4,France 5,War crimes in World War II 6,France's National Library 7,South Africa 8,Nelson Mandela 9,The wolf 10,Jim Crace 11,French 12,Actress 13,Tony Blair 14,43 15,William Pitt the Younger

QUIZ 129

ART & ENTERTAINMENT

1 Complete the TV show title; *NYPD* ----?

2 In which city was the show set?

3 Who said goodbye to the US *Tonight Show* in 1992?

4 Whose *Late Show* was a hit with US viewers?

5 In which country was *Shortland Street* a hit?

6 Almost rivalling Australia's *Home and* -----?

7 Which BBC 'soap' failed to hit gold?

8 In which country was it set?

9 What had the BBC built there at a cost of £2 million?

10 Which 'Martin' became a classic drama series success?

11 Who was the author of the 19th-century novel?

12 Which Paul starred in the series?

13 Which murder suspect was shown on TV being driven along a freeway in 1994?

14 In which city?

15 Which sport featured in an 18-hour US documentary in 1994?

ANSWERS

1, *Blue* 2, New York 3, Johnny Carson 4, David Letterman 5, New Zealand 6, *Away* 7, *Eldorado* 8, Spain 9, A holiday village 10, *Martin Chuzzlewit* 11, Charles Dickens 12, Paul Scofield 13, O J Simpson 14, Los Angeles 15, Baseball

QUIZ 130

PEOPLE

DIANA, PRINCESS OF WALES

1 What year did Diana die?

2 What year had she and Prince Charles married?

3 Where was the wedding?

4 Which London palace became her favourite?

5 Where was she pictured alone in the desert in 1992?

6 On what trip were the royal couple nicknamed 'The Glums' by the Press?

7 Which book first made public Diana's 'attempts at suicide'?

8 Who said 'I always believed the Press would kill her'?

9 What model of car was she travelling in when the fatal accident occurred?

10 On which BBC TV current events programme did she appear in 1995?

11 With which sportsman was she linked in 1996 by certain press reports?

12 Where were her two sons when told of Diana's death?

13 Who sang *Candle In the Wind* at her funeral?

14 What year did her brother succeed to her father's title?

15 In which county was she buried?

ANSWERS

1, 1997 2, 1981 3, St Paul's Cathedral 4, Kensington Palace 5, Egypt 6, The 1992 visit to South Korea 7, *Diana: Her True Story* by Andrew Morton 8, Earl Spencer 9, A Mercedes 600 10, *Panorama* 11, Will Carling 12, Balmoral 13, Elton John 14, 1992 15, Northamptonshire

QUIZ 131

SPORT

ATHLETICS: CHAMPIONS AND EVENTS

1 100 metres champ Linford-----?

2 400 metres superstar Michael----?

3 Welsh hurdler Colin J-------?

4 Carl L----- could run and jump for the USA?

5 Yvonne -------, Scottish track star?

6 Merlene O-------, sprint queen?

7 Sally G----- of hurdling fame?

8 Roger B----- the 400-metre man?

9 A Kenyan moved to Denmark: Wilson-----?

10 World record 'hopper, stepper, jumper' Jonathan-----?

11 Pole vaulter Sergey B------?

12 Decathlete Dan of the USA?

13 Frankie from Namibia, very quick?

14 Fiona once of UK, now jumping for Italy?

15 Donovan from Canada, world's fastest man in 1996?

ANSWERS

1, Christie 2, Johnson 3, Jackson 4, Lewis 5, Murray 6, Ottey 7, Gunnell 8, Black 9, Kipketer 10, Edwards 11, Bubka 12, O'Brien 13, Fredericks 14, May 15, Bailey

QUIZ 132

WORLD EVENTS

1 Fernando Cardoso became president of------?

2 Numbers of cases of what disease passed 1 million in 1995?

3 Tariq Aziz represented which country?

4 In which country was the Kobe earthquake?

5 Where were more ancient cave paintings found?

6 In which country was the Sejm the parliament?

7 And who was that country's president in 1995?

8 Which country said farewell to UN peacekeepers?

9 Which famous bank collapsed?

10 And which 26-year-old was blamed?

11 Where was Aristide talking tough?

12 Which IRA leader met a president?

13 Which president?

14 And on which special day for Irish-Americans?

15 Which British leader did the meeting annoy?

ANSWERS

1, Brazil 2, AIDS 3, Iraq 4, Japan 5, France 6, Poland 7, Lech Walesa
8, Somalia 9, Barings 10, Nicholas Leeson 11, Haiti 12, Gerry Adams
13, Bill Clinton 14, St Patrick's Day 15, John Major

QUIZ 133

PEOPLE

HAROLD WILSON (WHO DIED IN 1995)

1 In what town was Harold Wilson born?

2 What was his first name?

3 At which university did he study and teach?

4 What was his favourite football team?

5 What notable achievement did he record in 1947?

6 Who was his rival for the Labour leadership in 1959?

7 When did Wilson become prime minister?

8 And when did he resign?

9 Which African colony caused him most difficulties?

10 What did he smoke: a) pipe b) cigars c) nothing

11 With which particular item of clothing was he asssociated?

12 What was his wife's first name?

13 Which islands were his favourite holiday home?

14 Which impressionist reguarly impersonated him on TV?

15 And which title did he take as a peer?

ANSWERS

1, Huddersfield 2, James 3, Oxford 4, Huddersfield Town 5, Youngest Cabinet minister (aged 31) of the 20th century 6, George Brown 7, 1964 8, 1976 9, Rhodesia 10, a) 11, Gannex raincoats 12, Mary 13, The Scillies 14, Mike Yarwood 15, Lord Wilson of Rievaulx

QUIZ 134

SCIENCE & TECHNOLOGY 1990

1 What was Landsat?

2 What was the 'uranium-thorium method' being used for?

3 Where did the Climatron reopen?

4 In which US city was Lincoln Park Zoo?

5 And which of its animals had new quarters this year?

6 Which Philippine island was struck by an earthquake?

7 What did the initials ODP stand for in oceanography?

8 Which central Asian lake was explored by a joint US-Soviet expedition?

9 How much of the Earth's fresh water does it hold: a) 20% b) 10% c) 5%?

10 What weather phenomenon caused damage in Britain in Jan-Feb this year?

11 Which famous bridge was 100 years old in 1990?

12 What do the initials UNEP stand for?

13 In 1990 which British botanist won a UNEP award?

14 What caught fire and burned 17 days in Hagersville, Canada?

15 What kind of animal was the endangered Spix's macaw?

ANSWERS

1, An earth-resources satellite 2, Dating in archaeology 3, Missouri Botanical Garden 4, Chicago 5, Big cats 6, Luzon 7, Ocean Drilling Program 8, Baikal 9, a)20% 10, Storm winds 11, Forth Railway Bridge 12, United Nations Environmental Program 13, David Bellamy 14, 14 million rubber tyres 15, A tropical bird

QUIZ 135

POT LUCK

1 In which country is the Eleven Cities Tour?

2 What is unusual about it?

3 Which European troops were patrolling Bangui in 1997?

4 And where is Bangui?

5 Which European country had its first 'mad cows' in 1997?

6 Which South American country had a president nicknamed 'El Loco'?

7 Where did the Mothers of Plazo de Mayo campaign?

8 Which Polish city celebrated its saint's 1000th anniversary?

9 Which US ship took to sea at the age of 200 in 1997?

10 What classic horse race did Benny the Dip win that year?

11 For which team did Scot Paul Lambert play in the Champions League cup final?

12 Which herb was welcomed as an effective treatment for depression?

13 What new doll came with her own dentist's chair?

14 And which accessory accompanied Share a Smile Becky?

15 What did John Lobb make: shoes, furniture or wigs?

ANSWERS

1, The Netherlands 2, It's on ice 3, French 4, Central African Republic 5, Germany 6, Ecuador 7, Argentina 8, Gdansk 9, USS *Constitution* 10, The Derby 11, Borussia Dortmund 12, St John's Wort 13, Dentist Barbie 14, A wheelchair 15, Shoes

QUIZ 136

WORLD EVENTS

1 Where was the Armed Islamic Group (or GIA) active?

2 In which country was UNITA fighting a war?

3 Where was Robert Bourassa a leading politician?

4 Which small country annoyed airlines by closing its Bonriki Airport?

5 Which newly formed republic used the litas as money?

6 Was Palau: a) a new country b) a language or c) the new capital of Fiji?

7 Where was Yoweri Museveni president?

8 Which ex-president's son became governor of Texas?

9 Who was Newt Gingrich?

10 Which German statesman died in 1992?

11 Who was president of the Board of Trade in John Mayor's 1992 government?

12 Where did Ong Teng Cheong succeed Wee Kim Wee in 1993?

13 In which country was UNOSOM II operating?

14 And what was it?

15 Which world-famous shipping insurer was in trouble in 1990?

ANSWERS

1, Algeria 2, Angola 3, Canada 4, Kiribati 5, Lithuania 6, A new country 7, Uganda 8, George W Bush 9, Republican politician and speaker of the US House of Representatives (1994) 10, Willy Brandt 11, Michael Heseltine 12, Singapore (as president) 13, Somalia 14, A UN peacekeeping force 15, Lloyd's of London

QUIZ 137

PEOPLE

TWO STARS: BOTH DIED IN 1997

1 For which country did Dennis Compton play cricket?

2 For which county did he play?

3 And who was his friend and batting partner there?

4 In which other game was he an international?

5 And for which famous club did he play that game?

6 Which part of his body was said to be on show in a bottle at Lord's?

7 Which hair preparation did he advertise?

8 And in what year did he score a record 3816 runs?

9 What nationality were James Stewart's forebears?

10 Where was he born: a)Texas b) Pennsylvania c) New Jersey?

11 In which film and play did he talk to an invisible rabbit?

12 Why was he at first rejected as a military pilot?

13 In which 1954 film was he 'confined' by a broken leg?

14 In which 1939 spoof Western did he partner Marlene Dietrich?

15 And in which 1953 film did he play the trombone?

ANSWERS

1, England 2, Middlesex 3, Bill Edrich 4, Soccer 5, Arsenal 6, His kneecap (removed by a surgeon) 7, Brylcreem 8, 1947 9, Irish 10, b) 11, *Harvey* 12, Too thin 13, *Rear Window* 14, *Destry Rides Again* 15, *The Glenn Miller Story*

QUIZ 138

ARTS & ENTERTAINMENT

1 Is Twyla Sharp a dancer or a country singer?

2 What do the initials NYCB mean to ballet fans?

3 Whose 1992 concert marked 30 years with his record company?

4 And the record company?

5 Whose 1992 solo album was called 'Us'?

6 Gilbert Roland died in 1994. Was he a musician or an actor?

7 For which sport had he trained as a youth?

8 What art form is Robert Frank best known for: photography, painting or writing?

9 Which pop painter featured in a 1994 Tate retrospective?

10 Which Venetian's painter 400th anniversary was marked that year (1994)?

11 For which TV show did Ted Danson win awards?

12 In which country could you have watched Tele 5 and Antena 3 in 1993?

13 Who was the Roseanne of *Roseanne?*

14 And who went on playing Mike Baldwin in *Coronation Street* through the 90's?

15 And which ex-*Carry On* star carried all before her in *EastEnders?*

ANSWERS

1, A dancer 2, New York City Ballet 3, Bob Dylan 4, Columbia 5, Peter Gabriel 6, Actor 7, Bull fighting 8, Photography 9, R B Kitaj 10, Tintoretto 11, *Cheers* 12, Spain 13, Roseanne Arnold 14, Johnny Briggs 15, Barbara Windsor

QUIZ 139

POT LUCK

1 Lady Haden-Guest is better known as actress – who?

2 What colour was Monica Lewinsky's notorious dress?

3 Argentina won the 1998 World Cup – true or false?

4 In which African cities were US embassies hit by terrorist bombs in 1998?

5 Which prime minister's wife announced in 1999 a forthcoming new arrival?

6 Which Harriet found herself out in the cold politically?

7 What did Oflot regulate?

8 Which American chaired the peace talks in Northern Ireland?

9 Which Disney character reached the age of 70 in 1998?

10 For which club did Michael Owen play soccer?

11 To what job was Wim Duisenberg appointed?

12 Where did a sculpture of a yellow sheep with a banana-like body go on public view?

13 Which former French film star campaigned for pets?

14 Which Dutch soccer star came to manage Chelsea?

15 And which other British club did he then move to, briefly?

ANSWERS

1, Jamie Lee Curtis 2, Blue 3, False 4, Nairobi and Dar Es Salaam 5, Tony Blair's wife, Cherie 6, Harriet Harman, who lost her Cabinet post 7, The National Lottery 8, Senator George Mitchell 9, Mickey Mouse 10, Liverpool 11, President of the European Central Bank 12, Liverpool 13, Brigitte Bardot 14, Ruud Gullit 15, Newcastle

QUIZ 140

STILL IN THE NEWS AS THE 90S ENDED

1 Former prime minister and pro-European?

2 Former prime minister and Euro-sceptic?

3 Would-be prime minister and ex-comprehensive schoolboy?

4 Former merchant navy steward now running things on a wider scale?

5 Contemplating re-marriage (allegedly) to a Royal Prince?

6 Edna Everage playing Fagin?

7 The actress who played Catwoman in *Batman Returns?*

8 The dame who left MI-5 to write her memoirs?

9 The Labour politician who admitted she liked caravan holidays?

10 The cricketer who made his first Test hundred at Trent Bridge in 1990?

11 The ex-England soccer coach who took Watford into the Premier League?

12 And the smooth sports presenter who swopped chairs?

13 The jockey who rode 7 winners in one afternoon?

14 The Tory who returned as MP for Kensington and Chelsea in 1999?

15 The Labour Social Security Secretary who shaved off his beard?

ANSWERS

1, Edward Heath 2, Margaret Thatcher 3, William Hague 4, John Prescott 5, The Duchess of York 6, Barry Humphries 7, Michelle Pfeiffer 8, Stella Rimington 9, Margaret Beckett 10, Mike Atherton 11, Graham Taylor 12, Des Lynam 13, Frankie Dettori 14, Michael Portillo 15, Alastair Darling

QUIZ 141

THE BOOK WORLD OF THE 90S

1 Who wrote *Our Age: A Portrait of a Generation?*

2 Whose novel *Possession* picked up a Booker Prize?

3 What was the NBA, which collapsed?

4 Which poet's bicentenary was celebrated in 1995?

5 Who wrote *The Biographer's Moustache?*

6 And who wrote *The Moor's Last Sigh?*

7 Which 19th-century prime minister had a new biographer in 1995?

8 Who was the biographer (himself a politician)?

9 Which British politician wrote a book about H G Wells?

10 Who was the subject of the book *Oswald's Tale?*

11 And the author?

12 The nationality of Marguerite Duras?

13 In which language was the novel *Of Love And Other Demons* originally published in 1994?

14 Author?

15 In which country was a new paperback series labelled 'Cloth Tiger'?

ANSWERS

1, Lord Annan 2, A S Byatt 3, The Net Book Agreement (in the UK, fixing prices) 4, John Keats 5, Kingsley Amis 6, Salman Rushdie 7, Gladstone 8, Roy Jenkins 9, Michael Foot 10, Lee Harvey Oswald 11, Norman Mailer 12, French 13, Spanish 14, Gabriel Garcia Marquez 15, China

QUIZ 142

WORLD EVENTS

THE UNITED KINGDOM

1 What government post was held by Douglas Hurd during the Major administration?

2 Which Labour leader died in 1994?

3 Whom had he succeeded?

4 Which Anglo-French link was officially opened in 1994?

5 Who said she was withdrawing from public life in 1993?

6 Which unpopular tax was abolished in 1991?

7 Which former SDP leader announced his retirement from Parliament?

8 Which politician had been nicknamed 'Tarzan'?

9 What did the initials ERM mean to moneymakers?

10 Which union was Bill Morris chosen to lead?

11 Whom did he succeed in 1991?

12 Why was 9 April 1992 a significant day?

13 Who became minister in charge of 'national heritage' in 1992?

14 Which royal couple separated that year?

15 Who fired mortar bombs at Downing Street in 1991?

ANSWERS

1. Foreign Secretary 2. John Smith 3. Neil Kinnock 4. The Channel Tunnel 5. Princess Diana 6. The poll tax (community charge) 7. David Owen 8. Michael Heseltine 9. Exchange rate mechanism 10. Transport and General Workers 11. Ron Todd 12. It was general election day 13. David Mellor 14. The Duke and Duchess of York 15. The IRA

QUIZ 143

SCIENCE & TECHNOLOGY

1 What crashed into Jupiter in July 1994?

2 And which spacecraft orbited the same planet in 1995?

3 What did astrologers Alan Hale and Thomas Bopp discover in 1995?

4 Where in 1996 did some scientists claim to have found proof of life?

5 What was the name of the 1998 craft which orbited the Moon?

6 What did it discover at the Moon's poles?

7 What was Zarya?

8 Where was Nozomi headed for?

9 Which country built this spacecraft?

10 Which planet did the Pathfinder fly to in 1997?

11 Which planned 1999 polar landing failed to happen?

12 Which planetary moon was suspected to contain frozen water?

13 What new propulsion system was tested in a spacecraft called Deep Space 1?

14 What did the 1998 US Commercial Space Act make legal?

15 What was a 'rockoon'?

ANSWERS

1, Bits of Comet Shoemaker-Levy 2, Galileo 3, Comet Hale-Bopp 4, Mars 5, Lunar Prospector 6, Ice 7, A Russian-built spacecraft launched in 1998 8, Mars 9, Japan 10, Mars 11, The Mars Polar Lander never reached Mars as planned (NASA lost it) 12, Europa 13, An ion engine 14, Private spaceflights 15, An amateur rocket launched from a balloon

QUIZ 144

PEOPLE

1 Which polar explorer died in 1999 aged 91?

2 Which 'last great journey on Earth' had he led in 1958?

3 Which former Arsenal skipper and Manchester City boss died in 1990?

4 Which manager substituted England's second-highest goal scorer in a 1992 international?

5 Who was the player?

6 And whose record did he finish one goal behind?

7 For whom did Kapil Dev play internationally?

8 And in what sport?

9 Who had 1994 hits with *Pray* and *Relight My Fire?*

10 Who was Mae Jemison, in the news in 1992?

11 Which sport did Mike Krzyzewski coach?

12 What nationality was musician Youssou N'Dour?

13 Which racing driver won the first 5 races of the 1992 season?

14 Who wrote *The English Patient?*

15 Where did Milan Panic (an American) become prime minister?

ANSWERS

1, Sir Vivian Fuchs 2, The first land crossing of Antarctica 3, Joe Mercer 4, Graham Taylor 5, Gary Lineker 6, Bobby Charlton 7, India 8, Cricket 9, Take That 10, The first African-American woman astronaut 11, Basketball 12, Senegalese 13, Nigel Mansell 14, Michael Ondaatje 15, Yugoslavia (1992)

QUIZ 145

POT LUCK

1 How many countries adopted the euro in 1999?

2 Which country issued its first round stamp?

3 Which company's Pink Lotus Lamp fetched 2 million dollars at auction?

4 Whose portrait of himself without a beard was sold in 1998?

5 Who or what was the Russian Zarya?

6 For which sport was the Indira Gandhi Gold Cup awarded?

7 Why was the 1998 Kingston Test match abandoned after 61 balls?

8 In which North American city is the Thunderbird Stadium?

9 In which country was 90s star Nicole Kidman born?

10 Which singer made a fast-selling album called *Sevens?*

11 Which institution issued a Green Top 10 Plan?

12 Why was 'Mother Russia' in trouble?

13 Whose voyage did the *The Matthew* recreate in 1997?

14 Who was disqualified for ear-biting ?

15 And whose ear did he bite?

ANSWERS

1, Eleven 2, France 3, Tiffany 4, Van Gogh 5, A spacecraft 6, Hockey 7, The pitch was considered dangerous 8, Vancouver 9, Australia 10, Garth Brooks 11, The World Bank 12, The huge statue was reported to be cracking 13, John Cabot's from Bristol to Newfoundland, 1497 14, Mike Tyson 15, Evander Holyfield's

QUIZ 146

PEOPLE

1 For which soccer club did young England newcomer Steven Gerrard play in 1999?

2 Which 'screaming' pop singer turned parliamentary candidate died in 1999?

3 Which party did he campaign for?

4 Which political party did Dr Alan Sked lead?

5 With whom did Melanie Blatt sing?

6 Whose half-sister was Lauren Booth?

7 Who was the first Benedictine to be Archbishop of Westminster?

8 What game did Mark Ramprakash play?

9 What did Brian Jones and Bertrand Piccard do together in 1999?

10 Which ex-captain of England's soccer team died in 1994?

11 Who starred as US union boss Jimmy Hoffa in a 1992 film called *Hoffa?*

12 In which TV soap did Denise Welch become a regular?

13 For what did Lesley Garrett become famous?

14 Who hosted *Countdown* on TV?

15 And whose role as Compo ended with his death?

ANSWERS

1, Liverpool 2, Screaming Lord Sutch 3, The Official Monster Raving Loony Party 4, The UK Independence Party 5, All Saints 6, Cherie Blair's 7, Basil Hume 8, Cricket 9, They flew around the world in a balloon 10, Billy Wright 11, Jack Nicholson 12, *Coronation Street* 13, Singing 14, Richard Whiteley 15, Bill Owen (of *Last of the Summer Wine*)

QUIZ 147

POT LUCK

1 Which international soccer team did Colin Murphy coach in 1997?

2 Which Jason was a star for Harlequins and England?

3 On which island was filmmaker Anthony Mingella born?

4 On what occasion did he say it was a great day for his birthplace?

5 Which MP twice announced she was a lesbian?

6 Who compered his last *Mastermind?*

7 Which *Coronation Street* actor quit saying 'there's too much sex'?

8 Who said drink made him a 'violent bore' so he quit drinking?

9 Which fashion designer's funeral was held in Milan's Duomo?

10 He wrote *A Dance To The Music Of Time,* filmed for TV in 1997. Who was he?

11 Which 'Alice' author's centenary fell in 1998?

12 Which country hosted the 1998 Eurovision Song Contest?

13 Which song had earned it this 'honour'?

14 And the singers?

15 Who allegedly said of whom 'they'll be wanting golden elephants next'?

ANSWERS

1. Vietnam 2. Rugby player Jason Leonard 3. Isle of Wight 4. The 1997 Oscar ceremony 5. Angela Eagle 6. Magnus Magnusson 7. Bill Waddington (Percy Sugden) 8. Billy Connolly 9. Gianni Versace 10. Anthony Powell 11. Lewis Carroll 12. UK 13. *Love Shine A Light* 14. Katrina and the Waves 15. Clare Short, of Montserrat's requests for aid

QUIZ 148

SPORT

1 Which boxer regained in 1994 a title he'd lost in the 70s?

2 Which British boxer won a world title in 1995 by beating Oliver McCall?

3 Complete the name : Atlanta-------(baseball)?

4 And (same sport) : Colorado------?

5 Who was Australia's cricket captain in 1994-95?

6 Which batting brothers starred for his team?

7 Which Dominic was hailed as 'the new Botham'?

8 In which sport was the Fiesta Bowl a highlight?

9 In which game was the name of Jean-Marc Bosman causing discussion?

10 Why?

11 Which British soccer club won its first championship since 1914 in 1995?

12 Which Zimbabwean was among the world's top golfers of the mid 90s?

13 What sport did Glen Osborne play?

14 And for which country?

15 What game did the New Jersey Devils play?

ANSWERS

1, George Foreman 2, Frank Bruno 3, Braves 4, Rockies 5, Mark Taylor 6, Steve and Mark Waugh 7, Dominic Cork 8, American football 9, Soccer 10, He challenged the legality of the transfer fee system 11, Blackburn Rovers 12, Nick Price 13, Rugby Union 14, New Zealand 15, Ice hockey

QUIZ 149

ARTS & ENTERTAINMENT

1 What role did Geena Davis play in *Cut-throat Island?*

2 Complete the 1991 film title: *Don't tell Mom the Babysitter's*----?

3 What kind of disaster featured in the film *Dante's Peak?*

4 Who wrote *Haroun and the Sea of Stories,* for children?

5 What British quiz show was hosted by Regis Philbin in the USA?

6 Who was the show's presenter in Britain?

7 In which country was the 1995 film *Circle of Friends* set?

8 Where was the 48th Bienniale held in 1999?

9 The US National Gallery exhibited works by Alfred Stieglitz: was he a) a painter b) a photographer c) a cartoonist?

10 In which British city was the new Dean Gallery?

11 Which former world leader was the subject of a 1999 biography entitled *Dutch?*

12 Was it Kirk or Michael Douglas in the film *Greedy* (1994)?

13 In what arts body did Michael Kaiser become top man?

14 Which 60s survivor released an album called *Vagabond Ways?*

15 Whose *Sounds of the Suburbs* was screened on Channel 4?

ANSWERS

1, A female pirate 2, *Dead* 3, A volcano 4, Salman Rushdie 5, *Who Wants To Be A Millionaire?* 6, Chris Tarrant 7, Ireland 8, Venice 9, b) 10, Edinburgh 11, Ronald Reagan 12, Kirk 13, The Royal Opera House 14, Marianne Faithful 15, John Peel

QUIZ 150

PEOPLE

1 Who became Scotland's deputy chief minister?

2 For what was Rick Steyn best known?

3 What was Kriss Akabusi before he turned to TV?

4 What was Ann Swithinbank's area of expertise?

5 Which soccer club did Harry Redknapp manage?

6 And who did his son play for as the 90s ended?

7 Which ex-barrister became a TV chat show host?

8 Who was the controversial leader of the Nation of Islam?

9 Which sports star appeared with Bugs Bunny in *Space Jam?*

10 Who won a Golden Globe for his performance in *Casino?*

11 Where did publisher Steve Forbes run for president?

12 Who was Thomas Hamilton?

13 Which Scot was UK Foreign Secretary in 1996?

14 And which Scot held the job in 1997?

15 For which country did Frederik Deburghgraeve win its first-ever Olympic swimming gold medal?

ANSWERS

1, Jim Wallace 2, Cooking and restaurant-owning 3, A top athlete 4, Gardening 5, West Ham 6, Jamie Redknapp was with Liverpool 7, Clive Anderson 8, Rev. Louis Farrakhan 9, Michael Jordan 10, Sharon Stone 11, The USA 12, The Dunblane murderer 13, Malcolm Rifkind 14, Robin Cook 15, Belgium (1996)

QUIZ 151

POT LUCK

1 Which West Indian island was blanketed by ash?

2 What volcano was the culprit?

3 What was the name of the famous cloned sheep?

4 By what name did Daniel Hooper become an eco-warrior celebrity?

5 How many Teletubbies were there?

6 Which had the shortest name?

7 Which of the Spice Girls was blonde?

8 What kind of animal was Downing Street's Humphrey?

9 Which heroine of the game 'Tomb Raider' became a celebrity?

10 Which Labour peer had a dog named Buster?

11 What job did Betty Boothroyd hold?

12 To whom was Ed Balls chief aide?

13 Whom did he marry in 1998?

14 Was the wedding in a) Edinburgh b) Eastbourne c) Las Vegas?

15 Who named his son Prince Michael Jr?

ANSWERS

1. Montserrat 2. Soufriere 3. Dolly 4. Swampy 5. Four 6. Po 7. Baby (Emma Bunton) 8. A cat 9. Lara Croft 10. Lord Hattersley 11. Speaker of the House of Commons 12. Gordon Brown 13. MP Yvette Cooper 14. b) 15. Michael Jackson

QUIZ 152

ARTS & ENTERTAINMENT

1 Which Redgrave became a US citizen?

2 Which US actress announced her retirement in 1998?

3 Which film became the top-grossing UK production?

4 Which British-born American comic became an honorary knight?

5 Which *Friends* star had a baby in 1998?

6 Who played Oscar Wilde in a film?

7 And who co-starred as Lord 'Bosie' Douglas?

8 What job did Matt Dillon portray in *Wild Things?*

9 In which Henry James adaptation did Helena Bonham-Carter star?

10 In which film did Leonardo di Caprio play Jack Dawson?

11 Who played Cal Hockley in this film?

12 Who played a radio astronomer in *Contact?*

13 What was *Event Horizon* in the film of this title?

14 Which whale had a third cinema outing?

15 Which novelist did Michael Gambon play in *The Gambler?*

ANSWERS

1, Lynn 2, Jane Fonda 3, *The Full Monty* 4, Bob Hope 5, Lisa Kudrow 6, Stephen Fry 7, Jude Law 8, A sex councillor 9, *The Wings of the Dove* 10, *Titanic* 11, Billy Zane 12, Jodie Foster 13, A lost spaceship 14, Willy in *Free Willy 3* 15, Fyodor Dostoyevsky

QUIZ 153

SPORT

1 Which country did Francois Pienaar captain at rugby?

2 Which American city did the Cowboys come from?

3 And which game did they play: a) American football c) basketball d) baseball

4 Is Martina Hingis German, Swiss or Dutch?

5 And does she play tennis or golf?

6 In which sport did Atle Skaardal of Norway win his first world title?

7 In which sport was Michelle Kwan (USA) a star?

8 What year did she win a world title?

9 Who beat Tyson to win the WBA crown in 1996?

10 In which sport was Oscar de la Hoya a champion?

11 Which countries hosted the 1998 Cricket World Cup?

12 Who won the tournament?

13 What did the Quebec Nordiques ice hockey team become before the 95-96 season?

14 In which sport was Takanohana a *yokozuna?*

15 Which country did Jeff Rabkin represent at bowls in a world final?

ANSWERS

1, South Africa 2, Dallas 3, a) 4, Swiss 5, Tennis 6, Skiing (Alpine supergiant slalom) 7, Ice skating 8, 1996 9, Evander Holyfield 10, Boxing 11, India, Pakistan and Sri Lanka 12, Sri Lanka 13, The Colorado Avalanche 14, Sumo wrestling 15, Israel

QUIZ 154

POT LUCK

1 Who reworked his 'Candle in the Wind' for a funeral?

2 For whose funeral?

3 Who said he'd like to work without a wig?

4 Which politician wore a lounge suit to a white-tie do?

5 Who lost his seat at Tatton?

6 What sport was run by Bernie Ecclestone?

7 Outside which palace did flowers pile up in 1997?

8 Which world leader hurt his knee and had to be carried onto his presidential jet?

9 In which city did the Queen wear blue socks (and no shoes)?

10 What was she doing?

11 Who fled as leader of Zaire after 32 years?

12 Which veteran German fighter fell to earth in 1997?

13 Who drove Thrust SCC?

14 And what was it?

15 What was Thierry Dubois doing when rescued?

ANSWERS

1, Elton John 2, Diana, Princess of Wales 3, Lord Irvine, Lord Chancellor 4, Gordon Brown 5, Neil Hamilton 6, Formula One racing 7, Kensington Palace 8, Bill Clinton 9, Islamabad 10, Visiting a mosque 11, President Mobutu 12, A Messerschmitt 109 13, Andy Green 14, A jet car 15, Sailing solo in a yacht off Australia

QUIZ 155

HOW ARE YOU ON COMPUTER-SPEAK?

1 'Boot' means----?

2 BASIC is a ------?

3 DTP stands for?

4 dpi = ?

5 DP stands for?

6 LAN = ?

7 MS-DOS = ?

8 WYSIWYG means?

9 VDU = ?

10 Trojan Horse is a kind of -----what?

11 QWERTY denotes what arrangement?

12 Pixel is an abbreviation for----?

13 Laptops are -------?

14 A 'dongle' is a ------?

15 CAD stands for -----?

ANSWERS

1, To switch on 2, Computer language 3, Desk Top Publishing 4, dots per inch 5, Data processing 6, Local Area Network 7, Microsoft Disc Operating System 8, 'What you see is what you get' 9, Visual Display Unit 10, A kind of virus 11, The usual set up of keyboard characters, as on a typewriter 12, Picture Element 13, Portable computers 14, Copy protection device on a serial port 15, Computer-aided design

QUIZ 156

ARTS & ENTERTAINMENT

1 Which actor starred in a remake of *Lolita?*

2 In which film was Tommy Lee Jones 'Agent K'?

3 Which cartoon character did Leslie Nielsen play?

4 Who was Julianne in *My Best Friend's Wedding?*

5 In which city was *Nil By Mouth* set?

6 Who starred in *The Postman?*

7 What was the setting?

8 Which top star played a mountaineer in *Seven Years in Tibet?*

9 In which film did 'President James Marshall' appear?

10 And who played him?

11 Who played the terrorist leader in this film?

12 What was *Amistad?*

13 And who directed a film about it?

14 Who voiced the heroine in the cartoon *Anastasia?*

15 Which character was seen going to the USA on a job for the National Gallery?

ANSWERS

1, Jeromy Irons 2, *Men in Black* 3, Mr Magoo 4, Julia Roberts 5, London (Deptford) 6, Kevin Costner 7, A war-ravaged world in 2013 8, Brad Pitt 9, *Air Force One* 10, Harrison Ford 11, Gary Oldman 12, A slave ship 13, Steven Spielberg 14, Meg Ryan 15, Mr Bean in *Bean*

SCIENCE & TECHNOLOGY

1 On which planet was volcanic ash discovered?

2 Which planet was confirmed as having an 18th moon?

3 Was the new moon the planet's biggest or smallest?

4 Which was the most expensive scientific instrument of all time?

5 Did it cost a) 500 million US dollars b) 1 billion dollars c) 1.5 billion dollars?

6 Columbia , Atlantis and Discovery were all ……..what?

7 What nationality was the first journalist in space (1990)?

8 Which giant seabirds were tracked by radio and satellite to see how far they flew?

9 Which animal pets were given experimental bleeper-collars to warn birds?

10 How many 90s years were in the top ten temperature-wise?

11 In which continent were the oldest-known organisms discovered in 1997?

12 Were they algae, corals or trees?

13 Britain's rarest crow was facing extinction - what is it?

14 Which African insects crossed from Mexico into the USA in 1990?

15 Bosons made news in 1990: are they subatomic particles, distant stars, or missiles?

ANSWERS

1, Venus 2, Saturn 3, Smallest 4, The Hubble space telescope 5, c) 6, US space shuttles 7, Japanese 8, Wandering albatrosses 9, Cats (in a 1999 trial) 10, Four 11, Australia 12, Algae 13, Chough 14, Bees 15, Subatomic particles

QUIZ 158

POT LUCK

1 What unusual family record did Dale Wright achieve in 1997 at the age of 29?

2 Who named a crab, Peter?

3 What record did Andy Green break?

4 Which Tory was called a 'potbellied old soak'?

5 By whom?

6 And what post did the insult-giving politician briefly hold?

7 Which Harrods boss bought 'a Cottage'?

8 Over which building did a flag fly at half-mast, breaking a royal tradition?

9 Who launched a royal website?

10 Who won the right to be fertilized by her dead husband's sperm?

11 What bill did MP Mike Foster try to make law?

12 Which airline decided not to fly the flag?

13 Who retorted that his airline was 'British and proud of it'?

14 Who used her hankie to cover the tail of a model airliner to show disapproval?

15 Which new TV channel wasn't available to all UK viewers?

ANSWERS

1, He became Britain's youngest grandfather 2, John Prescott 3, World land speed record 4, Kenneth Clarke 5, Tony Banks 6, Sports Minister 7, Mohammed Al-Fayed who bought Fulham FC 8, Buckingham Palace 9, The Queen 10, Diane Blood 11, A ban on hunting with dogs 12, British Airways 13, Richard Branson 14, Mrs Thatcher 15, Channel 5

QUIZ 159

WORLD EVENTS

1 Which country did Meles Zenawi lead in 1991?

2 Who became first president of free Croatia?

3 Which country voted 'no' to EU membership in 1994?

4 Where was Ken Saro-Wiwa executed in 1995?

5 Whose headquarters were at Pale?

6 What was the majority population in Kosovo?

7 Who said a 'two-speed Europe' was likely?

8 To what was he/she referring?

9 What new fund-raiser began in November 1994 in Britain?

10 What post did Sir Patrick Mayhew occupy in 1995?

11 Who was John Briton?

12 Which country's currency was the manat?

13 Which new state's capital was Tashkent?

14 What was the NASDAQ index?

15 Who did Juanita Broaddrick accuse of sexual assault 21 years before?

ANSWERS

1, Ethiopia 2, Franjo Tudjman 3, Norway 4, Nigeria 5, Bosnian Serbs 6, Ethnic Albanians 7, John Major 8, Monetary union 9, The National Lottery 10, Northern Ireland Secretary 11, Irish prime minister 12, Turkmenistan 13, Uzbekistan 14, A stock market listing of hi-tech company shares 15, President Clinton

QUIZ 160

MUSIC

1 Who went straight to number one in 1994 with *Saturday Night?*

2 Who had a hit with *Goodnight Girl* in 1992?

3 Who said *My Name Is Prince?*

4 Who topped with *End of the Road* (1992)?

5 Who sang *Tom Traubert's Blues?*

6 What singer appeared in *The Bodyguard?*

7 Who had 27 consecutive Top 20 hits until 1993?

8 Who recorded the 1993 hit *No Limit?*

9 Whose *The Boy Is Mine* topped the US charts in 1998?

10 At the same time, whose *Viva Forever* was riding high in 1998?

11 *Rollercoaster* was a hit for------- who?

12 And who took *Believe* to number one in 1998?

13 Who recorded a 1998 solo album with 'Miseducation' in the title?

14 What did Teletubbies say in 1997?

15 And who sang *I Know Where It's At?*

ANSWERS

1, Whigfield 2, Wet Wet Wet 3, Prince 4, Boyz II Men 5, Rod Stewart
6, Whitney Houston 7, Madonna 8, 2 Unlimited 9, Brandy & Monica
10, Spice Girls 11, B*Witched 12, Cher 13, Lauryn Hill 14, *Eh-oh*
15, All Saints

QUIZ 161

WORLD EVENTS

1 Which is South America's largest nation?

2 And what was Mercosir, which it joined in the 90s?

3 What is the majority religion of Sri Lanka?

4 Where was Islam Karimov president?

5 Which country banned CFZ?

6 And what was it?

7 Where was the Great Hanshin Earthquake?

8 Where did Lamberto Dini seek power?

9 What year did Eritrea gain independence?

10 Where was Fuday Sankoh leading a revolt?

11 Which European river reached a 200-year high in 1995?

12 For whom was Mickey Kantor chief trade representative?

13 Where were the MPLA and UNITA in confrontation?

14 Where was the *People's Daily* published?

15 Who went to South Africa for the first time since 1947?

ANSWERS

1, Brazil 2, A common market 3, Buddhism 4, Uzbekistan 5, Australia
6, A pesticide 7, Japan 8, Italy 9, 1993 10, Sierra Leone 11, The Rhine
12, USA 13, Angola 14, China 15, The Queen

QUIZ 162

POT LUCK

1 Which British big cat was swallowed by Ford?

2 What had Terry Anderson and Terry Waite in common?

3 Who went on holiday and found the phones wouldn't work?

4 What was going on in his absence (1991)?

5 Who was told he looked 'wiped out' by a fellow leader?

6 Who was that leader?

7 From which post did Sir Alan Green resign?

8 Who unveiled the 'Citizens' Charter'?

9 Which Labour notables became 'lapsed' CND members?

10 Which prince was hit by a golf club in 1991?

11 Who were released in 1995 having been jailed in 1975 for a pub bombing?

12 Who said 'I never thought I'd jump so far and lose'?

13 Who'd beaten him?

14 In which event?

15 Whose foreign minister was Gianni De Michelis?

ANSWERS

1, Jaguar 2, They were both held hostage in Lebanon 3, Mikhail Gorbachev 4, An attempted coup in Russia 5, John Major 6, George Bush 7, UK Director of Public Prosecutions 8, John Major 9, Neil and Glenys Kinnock 10, Prince William 11, The Birmingham Six 12, Carl Lewis 13, Mike Powell 14, The long jump (1991 World Championships) 15, Italy's

QUIZ 163

PEOPLE

1 Which Hashemite ruler died in 1999?

2 On what did Paul Mellon spend his millions?

3 Who was Didier Deschamps?

4 Which American won his first Grand Slam tennis title in 1992?

5 At which Olympics did he win a gold medal?

6 Whom did he marry in 1997?

7 Who became Israel's prime minister in May 1999?

8 Was he born in a) Israel b) Lithuania c) USA?

9 Who was Lance Armstrong?

10 And which event did he win in 1999?

11 What did Sister Wendy Becket talk about on TV?

12 Did Andrea Boccelli sing, dance or score goals?

13 At which 1999 awards ceremony did he perform?

14 And with whom?

15 Where did Hugo Chavez become president?

ANSWERS

1, King Hussein of Jordan 2, Art and philanthropy 3, France's most-capped footballer 4, André Agassi 5, Atlanta 1996 6, Brooke Shields 7, Ehud Barak 8, a) 9, A US cyclist 10, The Tour de France 11, Art 12, He was an Italian opera singer 13, The Oscar ceromony 14, Celine Dion 15, Venezuela

QUIZ 164

SPORT

NAME THE SPORTS STARS' SPORTS

1 Tim Horan (Australia)
2 Phil Neville (England)
3 Jack Russell (England)
4 Rivaldo (Brazil)
5 Michael Klim (Australia)
6 Peter Nichol (Scotland)
7 Lindsay Davenport (USA)
8 Maurice Greene (USA)
9 Stephen Hendry (Scotland)
10 Gregor Townsend (Scotland)
11 Mikka Hakkinen (Finland)
12 Peter Gade Christensen (Denmark)
13 Dean Saunders (Wales)
14 Roy Keane (Ireland)
15 Rodrigo Pessoa (Brazil)

ANSWERS

1, Rugby football 2, Soccer 3, Cricket 4, Soccer 5, Swimming 6, Squash
7, Tennis 8, Athletics 9, Snooker 10, Rugby football 11, Motor racing
12, Badminton 13, Soccer 14, Soccer 15, Show jumping

QUIZ 165

WORLD EVENTS

UNITED KINGDOM IN 1995

1 Which Tory MP switched parties in 1990 to join Labour?

2 To which party did Emma Nicholson defect?

3 Who said 'put up or shut up'?

4 Which politician was nicknamed 'the Vulcan'?

5 Who resigned as UK Foreign Secretary in 1995?

6 Which cabinet minister left under a cloud and later went to jail?

7 Which party decided to abandon Clause 4?

8 Where did three prisoners get away by copying the jail's master key?

9 And who was Derek Lewis, who got the sack?

10 Who sacked him?

11 Which company owned the *Brent Spar?*

12 How much of the new UK National Lottery went on prizes?

13 How much (as a percentage) went to 'good causes'?

14 Who were suffering from 'negative equity'?

15 Which-long established bank's collapse caused ripples in the financial world?

ANSWERS

1, Alan Howarth 2, The Liberal Democrats 3, John Major 4, John Redwood 5, Douglas Hurd 6, Jonathan Aitken 7, Labour 8, Parkhurst 9, Director-general of the UK prison service 10, Michael Howard, then Home Secretary 11, Royal Dutch/Shell 12, Half 13, 28% 14, Homeowners with mortgages 15, Baring's

QUIZ 166

ARTS & ENTERTAINMENT

1 In which play did Geraldine McEwan play Lady Wishfort?

2 Which inventor was the subject of the book *Longitude?*

3 And what had he invented?

4 Who played him in a TV adaptation of the story?

5 This same actor had earlier won an award for his performance in which Ben Jonson play at the National Theatre?

6 Which actor 'defected' from a West End play three days after opening in 1995?

7 What was the play?

8 And what part was he playing?

9 Which Gilbert and Sullivan classic was jazzed up in 1995?

10 Who played Al Jolson on stage that year?

11 Which actor knight, and angling enthusiast, died in 1995?

12 Which ageing actor recorded Shakespearean speeches, at Prince Charles' request?

13 How old was US producer-director George Abbott when he died in 1995?

14 In dance theatre, what was SFB?

15 Where was a ballet director subject to death threats?

ANSWERS

1, *The Way of the World* 2, John Harrison 3, A marine clock or chronometer 4, Michael Gambon 5, Volpone 6, Stephen Fry 7, *Cell Mates* by Simon Gray 8, The spy George Blake 9, *The (Hot) Mikado* 10, Brian Conley 11, Sir Michael Horden 12, Robert Stephens 13, 107 14, San Francisco Ballet 15, In Russia (he was the director of the Mariinsky)

QUIZ 167

POT LUCK

1 What post in London did Dame Shirley Porter hold in 1991?

2 Which Polish leader visited the UK that year?

3 Who had a 6-minute ovation but kept silent?

4 Whose wife was named Raisa?

5 And whose wife was Nancy?

6 Of whom did their manager say 'They are dancers. No one shows his p-word'?

7 What kind of neckwear did these artists wear?

8 Christy, Naomi, Linda, Cindy: what were they all?

9 Who said 'Perfick' in a popular TV role?

10 The series?

11 Who married Larry Fortensky?

12 Who wore two pairs of tennis shorts but bared his midriff?

13 Who made a fortune singing in her underwear?

14 To whom was Sir Bernard Ingham press secretary?

15 What did he call his memoirs?

ANSWERS

1, Lord Mayor 2, Lech Walesa 3, Mrs Thatcher at the Tory Party Conference after her fall 4, Mikhail Gorbachev's 5, President Reagan 6, The Chippendales 7, Bow ties 8, Super models 9, David Jason as Pop Larkin 10, *The Darling Buds of May* 11, Elizabeth Taylor 12, Andre Agassi 13, Madonna 14, Mrs Thatcher 15, *Kill The Messenger*

QUIZ 168

WORLD EVENTS

1 Where was Bill Hayden governor general?

2 Who wished to abolish this office altogether?

3 Which island state was headed by Dame Nita Barrow?

4 And what year did she die?

5 Which country's currency was the Belarussian rubel?

6 Where were the Awami League in opposition?

7 Which country had a head of state named Romeo Le Blanc?

8 Which war began in December 1994?

9 Which country's scientists described it as 'the most polluted in the world'?

10 Where did the Banana Salvation Committee make news?

11 Which government was accused of genocide?

12 Which state's capital was Fangafale?

13 Where were tourists spending bahts?

14 Which Mediterranean island wanted to join the EU?

15 Which new country's capital was Chisinav?

ANSWERS

1, Australia 2, The republican movement 3, Barbados 4, 1995 5, Belarus 6, Bangladesh 7, Canada 8, The war in Chechnya 9, Poland 10, Saint Lucia 11, The Sudan 12, Tuvalu 13, Thailand 14, Malta 15, Moldova

QUIZ 169

SPORT

GOLF

1 Who won golf's Ryder Cup in 1991 and 1993?

2 Who won the 1995 event?

3 What is Ernie Els' homeland?

4 What year did the Curtis Cup result in a 9-9 tie?

5 He won the US Masters in 1984, and again in 1995. Who?

6 Who was the Open champion in 1991?

7 Who made his mark as US amateur champion in 1994?

8 Who came 4th in the 1998 Open aged only 17?

9 Which Fijian won the 1998 US PGA title?

10 By what name was Eldrick Woods better known?

11 Which Scott dominated the European tour in the 90s?

12 Who beat Payne Stewart to win the 1998 US Open?

13 Who at 58 announced he was leaving the majors scene after 40 years at the top?

14 Who won the Ryder Cup in 1999?

15 Who represented England (and won) in the 1998 World Cup?

ANSWERS

1, The USA 2, Europe 3, South Africa 4, 1994 5, Ben Crenshaw 6, Ian Baker-Finch 7, Tiger Woods 8, Justin Rose 9, Vijay Singh 10, 'Tiger' 11, Colin Montgomerie 12, Lee Janzen 13, Jack Nicklaus 14, USA 15, Nick Faldo and David Carter

QUIZ 170

TV & RADIO

1 In which TV series did Jessica investigate?

2 Who was the host of *Have I Got News For You?*

3 And in which sitcom did he also appear?

4 What radio show did Sue McGregor co-present?

5 And on which sport did Jonathan Agnew broadcast?

6 What sport did Clare Balding talk about?

7 On which TV show for kids did Katy Hill appear?

8 Richie, Sarah, Eric, Diana------all characters in?

9 Eddie, Clarrie, Phil, Jill-----all still going in which radio show?

10 Who presented *Animal Hospital?*

11 What kind of machines turned on Jeremy Clarkson?

12 Complete the TV title: *Still in Bed with----?*

13 And who presented *Open House* on Channel 5?

14 Steve, Vicky, Jim---- it must be, which soap?

15 For what were Conan O'Brien and Jay Leno becoming famous on US TV?

ANSWERS

1, *Murder, She Wrote* 2, Angus Deayton 3, *One Foot In The Grave* 4, *Today* on Radio 4 5, Cricket 6, Horse Racing 7, *Blue Peter* 8, *Emmerdale* 9, *The Archers* 10, Rolf Harris 11, Cars 12, *MeDinner* 13, Gloria Hunniford 14, *Coronation Street* 15, They were late-night talk-show hosts

QUIZ 171

POT LUCK

1 Which British woman won the 1991 New York Marathon?

2 Who described one of his products as 'total crap'?

3 Which sport did David Campese play?

4 Who was 'Stormin' Norman'?

5 Who was he: aristocratic Tory minister William W--------?

6 Who in 1991 broke an athletics record set in 1968?

7 Of what crimes was Jeffrey Dahmer accused?

8 What were found in his fridge?

9 Who replaced Gorbachev as Russia's leader?

10 What nationality is Aung San Su Kyi?

11 What prize was she awarded?

12 Who was sacked from Brent Walker in 1991?

13 In which sport had his brother been famous?

14 What did artist Christo set up in the USA and Japan?

15 Which tennis player came from 936th in the rankings to a semi-final in the US Open (1991)?

ANSWERS

1, Liz McColgan 2, Gerald Ratner 3, Rugby 4, General Norman Schwarzkopf 5, Waldegrave 6, Long jumper Mike Powell 7, Serial murder 8, Victim's heads 9, Boris Yeltsin 10, Burmese 11, Nobel Peace Prize 12, George Walker 13, Boxing (Billy Walker) 14, Thousands of umbrellas 15, Jimmy Connors

QUIZ 172

WORLD EVENTS

1 Where did pro-Moscow forces try to seize Vilnius in 1991?

2 Which country invaded Kuwait in August 1990?

3 Which country's King Olav V died in 1991?

4 Which aerospace giant planned to buy McDonnell Douglas in 1996?

5 Where did a 1996 mid-air collision kill 349 people (1996)?

6 Which part of Indonesia broke away at last to become independent?

7 Why did US Democrats suspend John Huang?

8 On what subject was the Scott Report published in Britain?

9 Which Tory MP was alleged to have received money from the owner of Harrods?

10 Which politician had his eyes coloured red in a 1996 poster?

11 What slogan accompanied the picture?

12 Where did Oginga Odinga form a new anti-government organisation in 1991?

13 In which affair did Linda Tripp appear as a key witness?

14 What was she alleged to have done?

15 What month and year did Labour return to power in Britain?

ANSWERS

1, Lithuania 2, Iraq 3, Norway's 4, Boeing 5, India 6, East Timor 7, He was accused of illegal fund-raising 8, The 'arms to Iraq' affair 9, Neil Hamilton 10, Tony Blair 11, 'New Labour, New Danger' 12, Kenya 13, The Lewinsky affair in the USA 14, Tape-recorded conversations with Monica Lewinsky 15, May 1997

QUIZ 173

POT LUCK

1 What post did James Baker hold in the USA?

2 Of what was Judge Clarence Thomas accused?

3 Who played the lead character in TV's *GBH?*

4 Who came home in 1991 after 1,943 days as a hostage?

5 Who was Leyla Gordievsky's husband?

6 Where did she come to be reunited with him?

7 What sporting gift did President Bush give John Major?

8 What was Major's gift in return?

9 Where was Britain's Symphony Hall?

10 Who broke his right arm playing polo?

11 Which royals visited the Canadian ship *Ottawa?*

12 And who set up a theatre company called 'Theatre Division'?

13 Which tenor sang in the rain in Hyde Park?

14 Which *Street* actor was accused of being boring by a newspaper?

15 Did he win or lose the resulting legal action?

ANSWERS

1, Secretary of State 2, Sexual harassment 3, Robert Lindsay 4, John McCarthy 5, Oleg Gordievsky, KGB double agent 6, The UK 7, A baseball bat 8, A cricket bat 9, Birmingham 10, Prince Charles 11, Princes William and Harry 12, Prince Edward 13, Luciano Pavarotti 14, Bill Roache (Ken Barlow) 15, He won £50,000 damages

QUIZ 174

TELEVISION

1 Who was Gregor Fisher's TV 'alias'?

2 Who co-starred as Hester and William Fields?

3 Name of the sitcom?

4 Which soap was set in Summer Bay?

5 Who played Nick Rowan in *Heartbeat?*

6 And who co-starred as wife Kate?

7 In what year was the series set originally?

8 Name the series in which Richard Griffiths played a restaurant-owning sleuth?

9 Name his character.

10 Which two actors played 'perfect scoundrels' (1990-92)?

11 Who played Deborah in *Men Behaving Badly?*

12 Who hosted his *House Party?*

13 What was the name of Del Boy's girlfriend?

14 And who played her?

15 Which Janet left the BBC in 1995?

ANSWERS

1, Rab C Nesbitt 2, Julia McKenzie and Anton Rodgers 3, *Fresh Fields* 4, *Home And Away* 5, Nick Berry 6, Niamh Cusack 7, 1964 8, *Pie In The Sky* 9, Henry Crabbe 10, Peter Bowles and Bryan Murray 11, Leslie Ash 12, Noel Edmonds 13, Raquel 14, Tessa Peake-Jones 15, Janet Street-Porter

QUIZ 175

SPORT

1 Which Frenchman came to Leeds in 1992?

2 With which club did he win League and Cup medals in the same season?

3 Which incident at Crystal Palace cost him a seven-month ban?

4 Gary Lineker was twice voted Footballer of the Year by sportswriters: for which club was he playing the second time (1992)?

5 Who set a new First Division scoring record in 1992-93?

6 For whom was he playing?

7 Who beat Sheffield Wednesday 7-1 in a 1995 record Premiership away win?

8 Which 1995 England match was abandoned after 21 minutes?

9 Which Wiltshire club reached the Premier League in 1991-92?

10 Which Spanish club won the European Cup in 1992?

11 And which Dutch star managed them?

12 Who became Sir Bobby in 1994?

13 Who became the outstanding Welsh winger of the 90s?

14 In which country were Colo Colo champions?

15 And which club signed Mathias Sammer from Inter-Milan in 1993?

ANSWERS

1, Eric Cantona 2, Manchester United 3, He attacked a fan 4, Tottenham Hotspur 5, Guy Whittingham 6, Portsmouth 7, Nottingham Forest 8, The game against Republic of Ireland in Dublin after crowd trouble 9, Swindon Town 10, Barcelona 11, Johann Cruyff 12, Bobby Charlton 13, Ryan Giggs 14, Chile 15, Borussia Dortmund

QUIZ 176

WORLD EVENTS

1 Which currency lost 3 zeros in value in 1998?
2 Which two Horn of Africa states were hostile?
3 Which country's prime minister was Lionel Jospin?
4 Which new country's capital was Zagreb?
5 By what name is the city of Lefkosia better known?
6 Which country's parliament is the Lok Sabha?
7 Which party controlled it after elections in 1998?
8 Which state's president was Ezer Weizman?
9 Where did the sight of women athletes cause controversy?
10 Where did a disco fire kill 68 in October 1998?
11 Which Chilean general found himself under arrest in London?
12 Who became Northern Ireland's deputy first minister in the new assembly?
13 Which president's wife decided to run for office herself?
14 Which UK port was in the news over 'asylum-seekers' arriving from the Balkans?
15 Which North African state had a new head of state after 38 years?

ANSWERS

1, The Russian ruble 2, Ethiopia and Eritrea 3, France 4, Croatia 5, Nicosia (Cyprus) 6, India's 7, The BJP (Bharatiya Janata Party) 8, Israel 9, Qatar 10, Gothenburg, Sweden 11, General Pinochet 12, Seamus Mallon 13, Hillary Clinton 14, Dover 15, Morocco

QUIZ 177

POT LUCK

1 With which band did Michael Hutchence sing?
2 Where was Israeli politician Chaim Herzog born?
3 For which English soccer club did Billy Bremner play?
4 And which club did he manage from 1989-92?
5 Which character did the Rev. Awdry (d.1997) create?
6 Who played the Riddler in *Batman Forever* (1995)?
7 Who developed the *Lord of the Dance* show?
8 Who was Henri Paul?
9 Who was MP for Richmond, North Yorkshire?
10 What did Intel Corp manufacture?
11 Which actor starred in *Regarding Henry* (1991)?
12 And in which 1992 film did he play a CIA agent?
13 Can you name the agent?
14 Where was the ECOMOG peacekeeping force in place?
15 And which country led it?

ANSWERS

1, INXS 2, Belfast 3, Leeds United 4, Doncaster Rovers 5, Thomas the Tank Engine 6, Jim Carrey 7, Michael Flatley 8, The driver of the car in which Princess Diana died 9, William Hague 10, Computer chips 11, Harrison Ford 12 *Patriot Games* 13, Jack Ryan 14, Sierra Leone 15, Nigeria

QUIZ 178

THEATRE & BOOKS

1 Which young playwright shocked audiences with her play *Blasted* (1995)?

2 How did her career end four years later?

3 Which veteran actor took off his clothes in *Prospero's Boots?*

4 In which 1996 TV series did this actor play 'The Professor of Sunlight'? (it was based on a Swift classic)

5 Who wrote about 'Discworld'?

6 Which TV inquisitor wrote about the English?

7 Who wrote *The Prisoner of Azkaban?*

8 And who was its celebrated boy-hero?

9 And who wrote about Sharpe?

10 Who played the Sharpe character on TV?

11 And in what historical period were the stories set?

12 In which 1996 Shakespeare production did a real-life father and son appear?

13 Who were they?

14 And which parts did they play?

15 The author of *The Day of The Jackal* became a CBE: who was he?

ANSWERS

1, Sarah Kane 2, She committed suicide 3, John Gielgud 4, *Gulliver's Travels* 5, Terry Pratchett 6, Jeremy Paxman 7, J K Rowling 8, Harry Potter 9, Bernard Cornwell 10, Sean Bean 11, The Napoleonic Wars 12, *Henry IV Parts One and Two* 13, Timothy and Samuel West 14, Falstaff and Hal 15, Frederick Forsyth

QUIZ 179

SPORT

1 Whose penalty kick did David Seaman save in the 1996 England v Scotland Euro 96 match?

2 And which team did England then beat 4–1?

3 Which club produced both Robbie Fowler and Michael Owen?

4 For what title were Adrian Maguire and John Reid competing in 1993–94?

5 What were Arrows?

6 Which English soccer club had Paul Jewell as their manager in 1999?

7 For which county did Mark Alleyne play cricket?

8 And for which country did Shivnarine Chanderpaul play?

9 Which national team did Keith Wood captain?

10 And in which sport?

11 Which Rugby League club played at The Valley?

12 What was Matthew Pinsent's sport?

13 Which runner was christened the Fife Flyer?

14 What game did Darren Clarke play?

15 And what did Carl Fogarty ride?

ANSWERS

1, Gary McAllister 2, Holland 3, Liverpool 4, Champion jockey 5, A Grand Prix racing team 6, Bradford City 7, Gloucestershire 8, West Indies 9, Ireland 10, Rugby Union 11, London Broncos 12, Rowing 13, Scots sprinter Ian Mackie 14, Golf 15, Moterbikes

QUIZ 180

POT LUCK

1 Where did Erling Kagge walk solo in 1993?

2 What fish was caught in the River Avon in 1991 for the first time in living memory?

3 Whom did Sophie Rhys-Jones marry in 1999?

4 What did the UK produce 100 million tons of every year?

5 What was Bill Cash MP sceptical about?

6 Which new London business centre was bombed in 1996?

7 Who quit as Ulster Unionist leader in 1995?

8 Who was sued for throwing gladioli on stage in 1999?

9 And who sued?

10 Why was Nick Brown often seen on the farm?

11 Which animals were to get passports?

12 Where did Richard Butler look for hidden weapons?

13 Where did the Prince of Wales Barracks change hands in 1997?

14 Which Disney hit about a lion became a stage musical?

15 For which UK political party was Matthew Taylor an MP?

ANSWERS

1, To the South Pole 2, A salmon 3, Prince Edward 4, Rubbish 5, The European Union (he was a leading Tory 'Euro-sceptic') 6, Canary Wharf 7, James Molyneaux 8, Dame Edna Everage 9, A member of the audience was hit in the eye (at a Melbourne concert) 10, He became UK Agriculture Minister 11, Pets (when quarantine laws ended) 12, Iraq 13, Hong Kong 14, *The Lion King* 15, Liberal Democrats

QUIZ 181

ARTS & ENTERTAINMENT

1 Who directed the film *Quiz Show?*

2 And who played the central character?

3 Can you name either this brainbox or the quiz show?

4 In the 1993 film *Sliver,* what was a sliver?

5 Who starred as a *'Kindergarten Cop'* in 1990?

6 And in which 1991 film did he play a robot trying to protect a child?

7 Which actors starred in *Hart to Hart* TV movies?

8 Where did the *Independence Day* invaders come from: a) Russia b) China c) outer space?

9 Who directed *Mission: Impossible?*

10 And who was its top male star?

11 Who played the father of a ransom victim in *Ransom?*

12 Who played Cruella De Vil?

13 And the film?

14 In which city was *Trainspotting* set?

15 What kind of band featured in *Brassed Off?*

ANSWERS

1, Robert Redford 2, Ralph Fiennes 3, Charles Van Doren, *Twenty One* 4, A thin apartment block in New York 5, Arnold Schwarzenegger 6, *Terminator 2: Judgment Day* 7, Robert Wagner and Stefanie Powers 8, Outer space 9, Brian De Palma 10, Tom Cruise 11, Mel Gibson 12, Glenn Close 13, *101 Dalmatians* 14, Edinburgh 15, A brass band

QUIZ 182

INTERNATIONAL SOCCER STARS: WHICH COUNTRY DID THEY PLAY FOR?

1 Rivaldo?

2 Collins?

3 Southall?

4 Davids?

5 Cafu?

6 Vieira?

7 Batistuta?

8 Littbarski?

9 Jensen?

10 Flo?

11 Riedle?

12 Houghton?

13 Saunders?

14 Del Piero?

15 Sullivan?

ANSWERS

1, Brazil 2, Scotland 3, Wales 4, Holland 5, Brazil 6, France 7, Argentina
8, Germany 9, Denmark 10, Norway 11, Germany 12, Republic of Ireland
13, Wales 14, Italy 15, Scotland

QUIZ 183

ARTS & ENTERTAINMENT

1 Whose 1990 debut album was called *Forever Your Girl?*

2 About which conflict did US director Ken Burns make an 11-hour TV documentary?

3 Which horror-film actor, born in Worksop, died in 1995?

4 Which part did he play in the Bond film *You Only Live Twice?*

5 Which Dutch painter's works could be seen at the Royal Academy, London, in 1990?

6 Which artist's *Portrait of Dr Gachet* set a 1990 auction record?

7 What percentage of record sales in 1990 was taken by LPs: 5%, 15% or 50%?

8 What style of music did the US group Public Enemy perform?

9 Which cellist returned home in 1990 from 16 years in exile?

10 Aaron Copland died in 1990: was he a painter, poet or composer?

11 What instrument did Stevie Ray Vaughan play?

12 His brother Jimmie played with a band called the Fabulous------. What?

13 Which singer became Elvis Presley's son-in-law?

14 Who recorded the single *Jesus To A Child* in 1996?

15 What kind of music did the Cherry Poppin' Daddies play?

ANSWERS

1, Paula Abdul 2, The American Civil War 3, Donald Pleasence 4, Blofeld
5, Frans Hals 6, Van Gogh 7, 5% 8, Rap 9, Mstislav Rostropovich
10, Composer 11, Guitar 12, Thunderbirds 13, Michael Jackson
14, George Michael 15, Swing

QUIZ 184

POT LUCK

1 Which actor-knight had a London theatre named after him?

2 What were the most famous creations of Nick Park?

3 If El Nino was warm, what was El Nina?

4 Which country was extending its Shinkansen?

5 And what was it?

6 What was QVC?

7 What 'nationality' was the Grand Prix tyre-maker Bridgestone?

8 Why were athletes Randy Barnes and Dennis Mitchell in trouble?

9 What kind of craft did Steve Fossett travel in?

10 Where was 'euroland'?

11 Which US author wrote *American Pastoral?*

12 Which disease was the biggest killer in the USA?

13 What new plane was named Typhoon?

14 What kind of music did Snoop Dogg and Jay-Z play?

15 Which American actor appeared in *The Iceman Cometh* in London?

ANSWERS

1, Sir John Gielgud 2, Wallace and Gromit 3, Cold 4, Japan 5, A high-speed rail link 6, A home-shopping cable network 7, Japanese 8, Suspected drug use 9, Balloons 10, The 11 countries of the EU using the euro currency 11, Philip Roth 12, Heart disease 13, Eurofighter 14, Hip-hop 15, Kevin Spacey

QUIZ 185

THEY ALL DIED IN 1999: FOR WHAT WERE THEY BEST KNOWN?

1 Sir Conrad Hunte?
2 Richard Kiley?
3 Desmond Llewellyn?
4 Edward F Mars?
5 Jack Lynch?
6 'Boxcar Willie'?
7 Julius Nyerere?
8 Jennifer Patterson?
9 Jim Peters?
10 Guido Pontecorvo?
11 Willie Whitelaw?
12 Gene Sarazen?
13 Sylvia Sidney?
14 Augustus Pablo?
15 Rafael Alberti?

ANSWERS

1, West Indian cricketer 2, American actor 3, British actor 4, American confectionery tycoon (the Mars bar) 5, Irish politician 6, American singer 7, Tanzanian politician 8, British cook and TV celebrity 9, British athlete 10, Italian geneticist 11, British politician 12, American golfer 13, American actress 14, Jamaican reggae musician 15, Spanish poet

QUIZ 186

ARTS & ENTERTAINMENT

1 What kind of creature was 'Z', in a 1998 cartoon film?

2 Which US city featured in the film *Robocop 2?*

3 Who played the metallic law enforcer?

4 Who played two thieves in *Blood and Wine?*

5 Who was the Knight Rider in the TV movie?

6 Who played the ageing cop in *The Rookie?*

7 Who played a detective in *Murder at 1600* (1997)?

8 Who played a radio DJ in *The Fisher King?*

9 Who starred in *The Gingerbread Man?*

10 Who wrote the original thriller of this title?

11 In which 1996 film of a Henry James novel did Nicole Kidman play an heiress?

12 In which 1996 Jane Austen film adaptation did Gwyneth Paltrow star?

13 Complete the Kevin Costner title: *Robin Hood:* ------------?

14 Which film continued the *Peter Pan* story?

15 Who directed the 1991 film *Jungle Fever?*

ANSWERS

1, An ant (in *Antz*) 2, Detroit 3, Peter Weller 4, Michael Caine and Jack Nicholson 5, David Hasselhoff 6, Clint Eastwood 7, Wesley Snipes 8, Jeff Bridges 9, Kenneth Branagh 10, John Grisham 11, *The Portrait of a Lady* 12, *Emma* 13, *Prince of Thieves* 14, *Hook* 15, Spike Lee

QUIZ 187

POT LUCK

1 Which 500-year-old skin surprised archaeologists in London in 1999?

2 Why?

3 What was the nickname of the circus contortionist John Ak (died 1999)?

4 How old is the universe, according to a 1999 revision by scientists?

5 In which part of the UK did Britain's last pit ponies work?

6 What year did the last two retire?

7 What unusual-coloured carnations went on sale for the first time in 1999?

8 Which ancient script did John Chadwick (died 1999) help decipher?

9 Which former England soccer manager died in 1999?

10 Who became Northern Ireland secretary, succeeding Mo Mowlam?

11 Who came on as an England substitute in a 1998 World Cup game and scored?

12 Who were England playing?

13 In what sport did Jane Couch win a 'British first' contest?

14 Who married Gaynor Regan?

15 What 1998 march brought farmers and hunters into London?

ANSWERS

1, A banana skin 2, It was the first Tudor banana - bananas were thought to have been imported only from the 1800s 3, The Frog King 4, 12 billion years 5, South Wales 6, 1999 7, Violet 8, Minoan Linear B 9, Sir Alf Ramsey 10, Peter Mandelson 11, Michael Owen 12, Romania 13, Women's professional boxing 14, Robin Cook 15, The Countryside Rally

QUIZ 188

SPORT

SOCCER: WORLD CUP

1 Who won the 1990 World Cup?

2 Who was the leading goal-scorer?

3 Which British striker scored 4 in the 1990 finals?

4 Which two players missed penalties in England's semi-final in 1990?

5 Which was the only British Isles teams in the 1994 World Cup finals?

6 Which team beat them in the second phase 2-0?

7 For which team did Taffarel keep goal?

8 For which team was Stoichkov a key striker?

9 And where did his team finish in World Cup 94?

10 Who were Britain's representatives in the 1998 World Cup finals?

11 Which African team topped its group, but then lost 1-4 to Denmark?

12 How did France beat Paraguay in 98?

13 What role did Barthez play in the French team?

14 How many present or future Chelsea players appeared in France's team for the 98 final?

15 And can you name them?

ANSWERS

1, West Germany 2, Schillaci (Italy) with 6 3, Gary Lineker 4, Stuart Pearce and Chris Waddle 5, Republic of Ireland 6, Holland 7, Brazil 8, Bulgaria 9, 4th 10, Scotland 11, Nigeria 12, 1-0 on the 'golden goal' 13, Goalkeeper 14, Three 15, Leboeuf, Desailly, Deschamps

QUIZ 189

WORLD EVENTS

1 What was the 'Y2K' problem?

2 What kind of disaster was Georges (1998)?

3 Which Special Prosecutor harried President Clinton?

4 Which government apologised to its indigenous peoples for misplaced aid programmes?

5 Which former South African president was in court in 1998?

6 In which African capital did food riots break out?

7 Which country planned to shut down its nuclear reactors by 2010?

8 Which river did Hungary and Slovakia agree to dam?

9 Whose intelligent agency was Mossad?

10 Where was the Biswa Ijitema held?

11 And what was it?

12 Which sportsmen were the first Americans to visit Iran since 1979?

13 Where did A B Vajpayee become prime minister?

14 Where was the country's central bank raided?

15 Where was Pristina?

ANSWERS

1, The millennium bug scare 2, A hurricane 3, Kenneth Starr 4, Canada
5, P W Botha 6, Harare, Zimbabwe 7, Sweden 8, The Danube 9, Israel's
10, Bangladesh 11, A gathering of Muslim faithful 12, A wrestling team
13, India 14, Japan 15, The capital of Kosovo

QUIZ 190

PEOPLE

1 Was Ry Cooder noted for a) piano playing b) guitar c) drums?

2 What happened to Noureddine Morceli in the 1996 Olympic 1500 metres?

3 What game did Doug Flutie play?

4 Who designed the new Great Court for the British Museum?

5 Which Asian airport had he also designed?

6 Which Canadian ice hockey star retired in 1999?

7 His number was retired too: what was it?

8 Who was Lauryn Hill?

9 And what was the title of her successful 1998 album?

10 In which blockbuster film did Jake Lloyd star?

11 And which character did he play?

12 Who starred as Rob Roy in 1995?

13 Who married Mathilde d'Udekem d'Acoz in 1999?

14 Who became Russia's president as the 90s closed?

15 And whom did he suceed?

ANSWERS

1, b) 2, He won the gold medal 3, American football 4, Sir Norman Foster
5, Hong Kong's Chek Lap Kok 6, Wayne Gretzky 7, 99 8, A US singer
9, *The Miseducation of Lauryn Hill* 10, *Star Wars: The Phantom Menace*
11, Anakin Skywalker 12, Liam Neeson 13, Prince Philippe of Belgium
14, Vladimir Putin 15, Boris Yeltsin

QUIZ 191

MUSIC OF 1997

1 Which ex-Beatle appeared on Michael Parkinson's chat show?

2 Who sang *2 Become 1?*

3 Which song took them to the top of the US charts two months later?

4 Who split, made *Bitter Sweet Symphony,* then split again?

5 Who recorded *Richard III* in 1997?

6 And who sang *Blood On the Dance Floor?*

7 Which 1997 US hit had an unusual initials-only title?

8 Which veteran singer-songwriter recorded *Time Out of Mind?*

9 Which Men were on top in September 1997?

10 And who were 'tubthumping'?

11 *I'll Be Missing You* featured Puff Daddy and --- who?

12 *Baby Can I Hold You* was a hit for ---?

13 Who were being 'Barbie girls'?

14 What country did this band come from?

15 Who sang live for the first time in Istanbul?

ANSWERS

1, Paul McCartney 2, The Spice Girls 3, *Wannabe* 4, Verve 5, Supergrass
6, Michael Jackson 7, G.H.E.T.T.O.U.T. 8, Bob Dylan 9, *Men In Black*
10, Chumbawamba 11, Faith Evans 12, Boyzone 13, Aqua 14, Denmark
15, The Spice Girls

QUIZ 192

PEOPLE

1 Which couple co-starred in the film *Days of Thunder?*

2 Which 1999 film appearances by them caused some voyeuristic excitement?

3 And which director's last film was it?

4 Which actor had 'Scotland Forever' tattooed on his arm?

5 And which event did he claim was the 'most important in his life'?

6 Which would-be US senator 'tested the water' in New York?

7 Where did Adrienne Clarkson become governor general?

8 What did Hicham El Guerrouj do best?

9 Who was Jonathan Ross?

10 What was Sir Norman Foster's profession?

11 What game did Peter Ebdon play?

12 Where did Jorg Haider's electoral success provoke reaction from outside?

13 Who flew in the Breitling Orbiter?

14 Who became Britain's first undisputed world heavyweight boxing champion of the 20th century?

15 Which new party leader in the UK was born in 1959 in Inverness?

ANSWERS

1, Tom Cruise and Nicole Kidman 2, *Eyes Wide Shut* 3, Stanley Kubrick 4, Sean Connery 5, The opening of the Scottish Parliament 6, Hillary Clinton 7, Canada 8, Run 9, A TV presenter and host 10, Architect 11, Snooker 12, Austria 13, Brian Jones and Bertrand Piccard 14, Lennox Lewis 15, Charles Kennedy

QUIZ 193

SPORT

SOCCER

1 What year were English clubs allowed back into Europe?

2 What did Oldham and Luton Town have to replace in 1991?

3 What year was the English Premier League launched?

4 How many clubs were members?

5 Which French team won the European Cup in 1993?

6 What kind of scandal prevented them defending it?

7 What was unusual about the outcome of the 1994 World Cup Final?

8 Who were the first club to do the English League and Cup 'double' twice?

9 What year did they achieve their second double?

10 Who scored the fastest-ever FA Cup goal in 1997?

11 Playing for?

12 Who scored 34 Premiership goals for Blackburn Rovers 1994-95?

13 Which English team won the Welsh Cup in 1999?

14 Who beat Scotland 2-1 in 1996, at New Britain?

15 Whom did Scotland beat by the same score in the 1990 World Cup finals?

ANSWERS

1, 1990 2, Their artificial pitches 3, 1992 4, 22 5, Marseille 6, A bribery investigation 7, It was the first to be decided on penalties 8, Manchester United 9, 1996 10, Roberto Di Matteo 11, Chelsea 12, Alan Shearer 13, Hereford United 14, The United States 15, Sweden

QUIZ 194

ARTS & ENTERTAINMENT

1 Which actor spent 'a year in Provence' on TV?

2 Who was the author of the book that spawned the TV series?

3 Which disc jockey got a 1990 knighthood?

4 In which TV series did Gary Webster replace Dennis Waterman?

5 And what was his character's name?

6 In which country was *The Boys From The Bush* set?

7 Who played Reg Toomer in this series?

8 And which Bush was uppermost in his mind?

9 What was 'Fitz's' full name?

10 And who played him on TV?

11 Which 18th-century writer did the same author portray on a tour of Scotland?

12 In which soap did Mavis and Derek appear?

13 Which character in this series did Sarah Lancashire play?

14 Which popular children's series was set in Nutwood?

15 And what pirate captain returned to the screen in an updated version?

ANSWERS

1, John Thaw 2, Peter Mayle 3, Jimmy Savile 4, *Minder* 5, Ray Daley
6, Australia 7, Tim Healey 8, Shepherd's Bush 9, Dr Edward Fitzgerald
10, Robbie Coltrane 11, Dr Samuel Johnson 12, *Coronation Street*
13, Raquel Wolstenhulme 14, *Rupert* 15, Captain Pugwash

QUIZ 195

THESE CELEBRITIES DIED IN 1999: WHAT DID THEY DO?

1 Ian Bannen?

2 'Jack' Bromwich?

3 Peter Brough?

4 Guy Mitchell?

5 Sir Alf Ramsey?

6 Mel Tormé?

7 Joseph Heller?

8 George Basil Hume?

9 Rod Hull?

10 Penelope Mortimer?

11 Cyril Washbrook?

12 Joe Dimaggio?

13 'Tom' Denning?

14 Rory Calhoun?

15 Indrani?

ANSWERS

1, Actor 2, Tennis player 3, Ventriloquist 4, Singer 5, Footballer and football manager 6, Singer 7, Novelist 8, Roman Catholic archbishop 9, Entertainer and puppeteer 10, Novelist 11, Cricketer 12, Baseball player 13, Judge 14, Actor 15, Dancer

QUIZ 196

ARTS & ENTERTAINMENT

1 Which much-loved American movie actor (Jimmy to his friends) died in 1997?

2 Another cinema hero died the preceding day (July 1 1997). Who was he?

3 Which bandleader had actor (1) portrayed in a biopic?

4 And in which role had he served during World War II?

5 Which detective did actor (2) play in *The Big Sleep?*

6 Who played Hana the nurse in *The English Patient?*

7 Who made a film of Shakespeare's *Much Ado About Nothing?*

8 Which black American actor co-starred in it?

9 Complete the 1992 book title: *Men Are From Mars*----------?

10 Who was the author and 'relationship guru'?

11 Which actress won a Golden Globe for *As Good As It Gets?*

12 Who was her male co-star in the film?

13 Which soap character did Ross Kemp play on TV?

14 On which American TV show did guests often fight each other?

15 Which TV broadcasting organization launched News 24 (1997)?

ANSWERS

1, James Stewart 2, Robert Mitchum 3, Glenn Miller 4, Army Air Force pilot 5, Philip Marlowe 6, Juliette Binoche 7, Kenneth Branagh 8, Denzel Washington 9, *Women Are From Venus* 10, John Gray 11, Helen Hunt 12, Jack Nicholson 13, Grant Mitchell of *EastEnders* 14, *The Jerry Springer Show* 15, The BBC

QUIZ 197

SPORT

SOCCER

1 Which team beat England on penalties to win the 1996 European Cup semi-final?

2 Where was the match played?

3 Who was in goal for England?

4 And which club had he joined in 1990 for a then-record fee?

5 Which London club had sold him?

6 What nationality was Enzo Scifo?

7 He returned to his original club in 1999. Which was it?

8 Which goalkeeper left Brondby for Manchester in 1991?

9 Which country did he represent?

10 Who left Anfield as the club's highest-ever scorer in 1996?

11 Which country was he capped for?

12 By what name was Romario Da Souza Faria better known?

13 What injury did he suffer in 1991?

14 Which Dutch club did he leave in 1993?

15 Which Spanish club did he then join?

ANSWERS

1, Germany 2, Wembley 3, David Seaman 4, Arsenal 5, QPR 6, Belgian
7, Anderlecht 8, Peter Schmeichel 9, Denmark 10, Ian Rush of Liverpool
11, Wales 12, Romario 13, A broken leg 14, PSV Eindhoven
15, Barcelona

QUIZ 198

SCIENCE & TECHNOLOGY

1 Where was the Biosphere 2 experiment?

2 How many people were involved?

3 What was it designed to replicate?

4 Which city banned taxis for one day a week in 1991?

5 Where was the Three Gorges Dam project?

6 What kind of fishing gear was called a 'wall of death'?

7 What animal was the US state of Montana trying to reintroduce after 50 years?

8 Which molluscs in tests learned to select balls by colour:
a) octopuses b) snails c) mussels?

9 Which new library's opening was delayed by rusting shelves?

10 What was unusual about the hooded pitohui bird?

11 Which famous genetic scientist resigned from the Human Genome Project in April 1992?

12 From which organization did Richard Truly resign the same year?

13 Which shuttle was new into space in 1992?

14 Was Ulysses a) a space probe b) a space station or c) a rocket?

15 Which Nobel prize did Georges Charpak win in 1992?

ANSWERS

1, Arizona 2, Eight 3, The Earth in miniature 4, Mexico City 5, China 6, Drift nets 7, The wolf 8, a) 9, The British Library 10, Its body contains a nerve toxin – it's poisonous! 11, James D Watson 12, NASA (he was Administrator) 13, Endeavour 14, a) 15, Physics

QUIZ 199

SPORT

1 Which game 'went professional' in 1995?

2 And which of its star players moved to Newcastle?

3 Which Irish runner became world cross-country champion?

4 Who won the 1992 Olympic 100m for men?

5 Which record score in the Premier League did Manchester United achieve in 1995?

6 Which England cricketer was noted for his off-the-field skill as an artist?

7 Who was Britain's best ever woman 400m hurdler?

8 Which netball international had two international footballing brothers?

9 And who were they?

10 Which Turkish club did Graeme Souness manage?

11 Which two London soccer teams shared Selhurst Park?

12 Which tennis player earned the nicknam 'Pistol-packin' Pete'?

13 In which sport was John Regis a star?

14 Who joined Lazio in 1992, a year late?

15 Why was his move held up?

ANSWERS

1, Rugby Union 2, Rob Andrew 3, Sonia Sullivan 4, Linford Christie 5, 9-0, beating Ipswich Town 6, Jack Russell 7, Sally Gunnell 8, Tracy Neville 9, Gary and Phil Neville (Man Utd and England) 10, Galatasaray 11, Wimbledon and Crystal Palace 12, Pete Sampras 13, Athletics 14, Paul Gascoigne 15, He had a serious knee injury, from the 1991 FA Cup final

QUIZ 200

SCIENCE & TECHNOLOGY

1 On the Internet, what is URL short for?

2 Which 'bug' was hyped as the scare of 1999?

3 And why were some people stocking up on food?

4 What was Linux?

5 In which country had it originated?

6 Which company introduced Dreamcast?

7 What did Matt Drudge do on the Net?

8 Is a WebCrawler a) a new kind of spider or b) a kind of indexer on the WorldWide Web?

9 What was the iMac?

10 How was MDTV different from ordinary TV?

11 Which company introduced Freeserve in the UK?

12 What were Tickle Me Elmo and Actimates Barney?

13 What did Tamagotchi mean in English?

14 And what were Tamagotchis?

15 Who or what was Zelda?

ANSWERS

1, Uniform Resource Locator 2, The Millennium Bug 3, There were alarmist fears that supermarket distribution and storage systems would break down because of computer problems. 4, A computer operating system 5, Finland 6, Sega 7, He was an Internet 'gossip columnist' 8, b) 9, The new Macintosh computer (1998) 10, It gave a sharper, clearer picture 11, Dixons 12, Toys 13, Cute little egg 14, Electronic 'virtual pets' 15, An electronic game from Nintendo

QUIZ 201

ARTS & ENTERTAINMENT

1 Who recorded *The Division Bell* album?

2 In the USA who chart-topped with *Bump N'Grind?*

3 Who composed the new opera *A Streetcar Named Desire?*

4 Which military band celebrated its 200th birthday in 1998?

5 Which Japanese, famous for his violin-teaching method, died in 1998?

6 Which 40s dance reappeared in the late 90s?

7 Which non-professional made a jazz film called *Wild Man Blues?*

8 And which instrument did he play in it?

9 Who was the singer/frontman of Pulp?

10 Were Manic Street Preachers a) Irish b) Welsh c) American?

11 Who played Cleopatra to Alan Rickman's Antony?

12 And in which play?

13 Which London theatre found itself with money + sponsorship problems in 1998?

14 From what part of the world did singer Baaba Maal come?

15 Who sang From This Moment On into the 1998 charts?

ANSWERS

1, Pink Floyd 2, R Kelly 3, André Previn 4, The US Marine Band 5, Shinichi Suzuki 6, The jitterbug 7, Woody Allen 8, Clarinet 9, Jarvis Cocker 10, b) 11, Helen Mirren 12, Shakespeare's *Antony and Cleopatra* 13, The Royal Court 14, Senegal, Africa 15, Shania Twain

QUIZ 202

SPORT

SOCCER

1 Which French soccer star could have had the new World Cup stadium named after him, but said no?

2 Who became Brazil's Minister of Sport in 1994?

3 Which Blackpool and England goal-scorer died in 1991 aged 69?

4 For which country did Roger Milla play?

5 How did he mark a goal?

6 What record did he set in 1994?

7 Which German international played in the 98 World Cup at the age of 37?

8 Which team did Paolo Maldini captain in the 98 World Cup?

9 Which Argentine international was banned in 1991 and 1994 for drug abuse?

10 Who scored Scotland's only goal in Euro 96?

11 Against whom?

12 Who made his 83rd and last appearance for the Republic of Ireland in 1997?

13 What national side had Michael Landrup in its line-up?

14 Which German striker joined Spurs in 1994?

15 With which club did he win a German league championship in 1997?

ANSWERS

1, Michel Platini 2, Pele 3, Stan Mortensen 4, Cameroon 5, He danced round the corner flag 6, Oldest player to appear in World Cup finals (42) 7, Lothar Mathaus 8, Italy 9, Diego Maradona 10, Ally McCoist 11, Switzerland (Scotland won 1-0) 12, Paul McGrath 13, Denmark 14, Jurgen Klinsman 15, Bayern Munich

QUIZ 203

PEOPLE

DIED IN 1999:

1 Who was known as 'The Yankee Clipper'?

2 What game did Godfrey Evans play?

3 In which 1970s cover-up was John Erlichman implicated?

4 Of which country was Amintore Fanfani six times prime minister?

5 Of which newspaper was Alastair Hetherington editor?

6 Whose stage companion was Emu?

7 Who was Britain's Chief Rabbi, for 1967 to 1991?

8 He directed *The Shining* (1990): name?

9 Hollywood actor nicknamed 'The Hunk': who was he?

10 How had a 1990 accident affected musician Curtis Mayfield?

11 He played the *Lone Ranger* in 1950s TV: who was he?

12 The author of *A Severed Head* (1961): who was she?

13 The star of the 60s musical *Stop The World-I Want To Get Off?*

14 Real name Mary O'Brien, profession: singer: who was she?

15 Which king died in Rabat?

ANSWERS

1, Joe Di Maggio 2, Cricket 3, Watergate 4, Italy 5, *The Guardian* 6, Rod Hull 7, Immanuel Jakabovits 8, Stanley Kubrik 9, Victor Mature 10, He was left paralysed from the waist down 11, Clayton Moore 12, Iris Murdoch 13, Anthony Newley 14, Dusty Springfield 15, King Hassan of Morocco

QUIZ 204

POT LUCK

1 Where did all 20 members of the Commission resign?

2 Who had been its president?

3 And who took over in his place?

4 Which was the first Harry Potter book: title please?

5 In which film did Eddie Murphy talk to animals?

6 For which British soccer club was Dennis Wise sometimes the only British player?

7 Who released an album called Come On Over?

8 For which English county did cricketer Wasim Akram play?

9 Who co-ran a public relations firm called R J H?

10 What nationality was painter Arthur Boyd?

11 'Wilt the Stilt' died in 1999: who was he?

12 What game did Neil Back play?

13 Which US astronaut and moon-walker died in a motorcycle accident in 1999?

14 Which outspoken Tory came back to the Commons in 1997 but died in 1999?

15 Which 1993 publication from his pen had become a sensational bestseller?

ANSWERS

1, The European Union 2, Jacques Santer 3, Romano Prodi 4, *Harry Potter and the Philosopher's Stone* 5, *Dr Doolittle* 6, Chelsea 7, Shania Twain 8, Lancashire 9, Sophie Rhys-Jones 10, Australian 11, US basketball star Wilt Chamberlain 12, Rugby 13, Charles (Pete) Conrad 14, Alan Clark 15, *His Diaries*

QUIZ 205

PEOPLE

1 Where was Paola queen?

2 What kind of music did Cecilia Bartoli sing?

3 What game did Chris Oti play?

4 Who said 'I sleep with my Oscar'?

5 Who wrote *A Clockwork Orange*, and died in 1993?

6 Where was Le Duc Anh president?

7 Did Butch Reynolds run, swim or play football?

8 What nationality was tennis star Mary Joe Fernandez?

9 What game was Fred Couples good at?

10 Who 'tuned in and dropped out' for the last time in 1996?

11 What game did Sol Campbell play?

12 Who was no longer Tiffany, but a chart-topper in 1999?

13 What did Isobel Lang do on BBC TV?

14 Which pop group did *Mamma Mia!* celebrate?

15 Which sports coach raised eyebrows by inviting a faith healer to join his squad?

ANSWERS

1, Belgium 2, Opera 3, Rugby 4, Emma Thompson 5, Anthony Burgess
6, Vietnam 7, He ran 8, American 9, Golf 10, Timothy O'Leary 11, Soccer
12, Martine McCutcheon 13, The weather 14, ABBA 15, Glenn Hoddle

QUIZ 206

SPORT

1996 OLYMPICS

1 Who won the men's 100 metres?

2 And whose world record did he beat?

3 Which British runner was disqualified in the 100m final?

4 Who was the first man to win both 200m and 400m at the same Olympics?

5 And in which event did he set a new world record?

6 Which woman athlete matched his feat?

7 Who reached the 200m final in her fifth Olympics?

8 Which country won its first (and last) gold medal at the 1996 Games?

9 How many athletes took part: a) 5,600 b) 7,800 c) 10,700?

10 What was unusual about the funding of the 96 Olympics?

11 What outrage spoiled things on 27 July in Centennial Park?

12 Which US athlete won his 9th gold medal?

13 In which sport did one competitor win 6 golds in 1996?

14 And she was?

15 Which British competitor collected his 4th gold in consecutive Olympics?

ANSWERS

1, Donovan Bailey 2, Leroy Burrell 3, Linford Christie 4, Michael Johnson 5, 200m 6, Marie-José Perec of France 7, Merlene Ottey 8, Hong Kong 9, c) 10, There was no government funding 11, A pipe bomb exploded, killing a bystander 12, Carl Lewis 13, Gymnastics 14, Alexey Nemov of Russia 15, Rower Steven Redgrave

QUIZ 207

POT LUCK

1 Which TV person's career was boosted by *Singled Out*: a) Jenny McCarthy b) Anthea Turner c) Carol Vorderman?

2 Which 1994 film was the last voyage for the original Star Trek crew?

3 Which TV personality was described as 'small but perfectly formidable?

4 Whose 1996 penalty miss led to a pizza-ad contract?

5 Which country withdrew the Nomad?

6 And what was it?

7 Who lost to Steffi Graf in the 1991 Wimbledon ladies final?

8 For whom did Billy Konchellah run?

9 Which army in the Gulf War was the 5th largest in the world?

10 Which maze celebrated 300 years of confusion?

11 What game did Earvin Johnson play?

12 And by what nickname did fans know him?

13 Which country had Africa's highest dam by 1996?

14 Whose widow was Jiang Qing (died 1991)?

15 Where was a new building's entrance inspired by Mickey Mouse's ears?

ANSWERS

1, a) Jenny McCarthy 2, *Star Trek: Generations* 3, Ruby Wax 4, Gareth Southgate 5, Australia 6, A new plane 7, Gabriela Sabatini 8, Kenya 9, Iraq's 10, Hampton Court (in 1991) 11, Basketball 12, Magic 13, Lesotho 14, Mao Zedong's 15, Disney Co's offices in Orlando, Florida

QUIZ 208

WORLD EVENTS

THE GULF WAR

1 Which event sparked the Gulf War in August 1990?

2 What was Iraq trying to seize?

3 What was the RDF?

4 Who sent it into action?

5 Was Iraq's army a) the world's 3rd largest b) 9th largest or c) 5th largest?

6 What were Scuds?

7 Which of these countries did not take part: Syria, Israel, Egypt?

8 Which non-combatant country received hits from Iraqi missiles?

9 What did it receive from the USA?

10 What was the code name for the Allied operation?

11 How many US aircraft carriers took part?

12 Which sea-launched missiles were fired into Iraq?

13 What was the Missouri?

14 To which country did over 100 Iraqi planes fly to safety?

15 Which country supplied the Daguet Division to the Allies?

ANSWERS

1, Iraq invaded Kuwait 2, Kuwaiti oilfields 3, The US Rapid Deployment Force 4, Pres. Bush 5, c) 6, Soviet missiles used by Iraq 7, Israel 8, Israel 9, Patriot anti-missile missiles 10, Desert Storm 11, Six 12, Tomahawk cruise missiles 13, A 1940s battleship 14, Iran 15, France

QUIZ 209

SCIENCE & TECHNOLOGY

1 Where were 26,000-year-old human footprints found in 1999?

2 What was the British Army's new Phoenix?

3 Where were fossil amphibian footprints bought by the government?

4 What contribution to science did Susan Helms make in 1994?

5 What kind of birds died mysteriously in large numbers on South Georgia?

6 Is it true that bacteria were found able to live at temperatures above 100°C?

7 In which continent was the 'strange bird of Udzungwa' discovered?

8 Was it a) like a partridge b) like an ostrich or c) like an owl?

9 What was prozac being used to treat?

10 Which Nobel prize had R.L.M. Synge (died 1994) been awarded in 1952?

11 Where was Europe's longest cable-stay bridge opened in 1991?

12 What kind of vehicle was the X2000?

13 Which Australian city had a new cross-harbour-tunnel?

14 What was the Bibliotheque de France?

15 A new study of dunnocks was published in 1990. What are dunnocks?

ANSWERS

1, France 2, A robot 'spy-plane' 3, Ireland 4, She was a Shuttle astronaut 5, King penguin chicks 6, Yes 7, Africa 8, a) 9, Depression 10, Chemistry 11, Dartford Crossing 12, A tilting train 13, Sydney 14, A new national library 15, Birds, also called hedge sparrows

QUIZ 210

POT LUCK

1 Who beat Bath 82-6 at Maine Road?

2 What raced from Sydney to Hobart?

3 What did 73% of consumers believe about advertisers?

4 Which airline company's situation was described by its chairman as 'dreadful' in 1995?

5 What is the AA-11 Archer?

6 What did Reebok, Kids and Timberland sell?

7 Where was Alain Juppé prime minister?

8 In what industry was Ted Turner a tycoon?

9 With which book series was RL Stine associated?

10 And who read them most avidly?

11 Which colony voted no to independence in 1995?

12 On what did Howard Cosell broadcast?

13 What nationality was writer William Robertson Davies?

14 Where was Jonah Lomu born?

15 What was South African Hugh Masekela: a writer, a musician or a rugby player?

ANSWERS

1, Wigan, playing Rugby League rules 2, Yachts 3, That they misled or exaggerated 4, Air France 5, A Russian air-to-air missile 6, Footwear 7, France 8, Media and broadcasting 9, *Goosebumps* 10, Children 11, Bermuda 12, Sport 13, Canadian 14, New Zealand 15, A musician

QUIZ 211

SCIENCE & TECHNOLOGY

1 Which was Europe's busiest container port?
2 In which country did the TGV run?
3 What is it?
4 In which country was a STAR 21 under development?
5 Was it: a) a car b) a ship c) a train?
6 What did the initials LRT stand for in the transport industry?
7 Which country had the largest rail network in 1990?
8 In which country did the AVE railway operate?
9 Which country was building the Great Belt crossing?
10 Which consortium built the A-330 aircraft?
11 And which was developing the 777?
12 Where was the Akashi Bridge?
13 Which islands was it built to link?
14 Which country had the most dams under construction in 1990?
15 Which car giant launched the Saturn in 1991?

ANSWERS

1, Rotterdam 2, France 3, A high-speed train 4, Japan 5, c) 6, Light Rail Transit 7, The USSR 8, Spain 9, Denmark 10, Airbus 11, Boeing 12, Japan 13, Honshu and Shikoku 14, China 15, General Motors

QUIZ 212

POT LUCK

1 What post did Willy Claes take on in 1994?

2 Which computer boss was hit in the face with a custard pie in 1998?

3 What sport did Ronaldo play?

4 Who was Ute Lemper?

5 Which Geordie actress won a Tony award in 1997?

6 Whom did Andrew Cunanan allegedly shoot dead in Miami in 1997?

7 In which new parliament was Lord Steel presiding?

8 Who bought a £40,000 engagement ring for her footballer fiancé?

9 And who had her estranged husband jailed for breaking her fingernail?

10 In which part of Britain was the Gavaghy Road in the news?

11 What kind of disaster was 'Mitch' (1998)?

12 What was lowered from 18 to 16?

13 Who was Zara Phillips?

14 Which royal ship sailed into retirement?

15 Who said 'I did something very foolish' after an evening on Clapham Common?

ANSWERS

1, NATO secretary-general 2, Bill Gates 3, Soccer 4, A German singer 5, Janet McTeer 6, Gianni Versace 7, Scotland's new Assembly 8, Victoria Adams (Posh Spice) 9, Pamela Anderson 10, Northern Ireland 11, A hurricane 12, The age of consent for homosexuals 13, Princess Anne's daughter 14 The royal yacht *Britannia* 15, Welsh Secretary Ron Davies

QUIZ 213

SCIENCE & TECHNOLOGY 1990

1 What was the name of the space telescope launched this year?

2 What did the initials COBE stand for to satellite watchers?

3 Which spacecraft reached Venus in 1990?

4 In which country was a new rail speed record set?

5 Where were Super Hikari under test?

6 And what were they?

7 Which river was spanned by the new Pont du Normandie?

8 Where did the Seabrook nuclear plant start operation: a) Australia b) UK c)USA?

9 Which of these countries had its first working nuclear power plant: a) India b) Nigeria c) Mexico?

10 What kind of weather phenomena caused much destruction across the USA?

11 ALACEs were released in 1990: what were they?

12 What was the new LTE 386/20?

13 What kind of machine was the new Ilyushin Il-96M?

14 From which country?

15 In 1991 Hasbro bought Tonka: what did these companies make?

ANSWERS

1, Hubble 2, Cosmic Background Explorer 3, Magellan 4, France 5, Japan 6, High-speed trains 7, The Seine 8, c) 9, c) 10, Tornadoes 11, Drifting instruments to trace ocean currents 12, A laptop computer 13, A transport aircraft 14, Russia 15, Toys

QUIZ 214

SCIENCE & TECHNOLOGY

1 According to a 1993 survey, what percentage of men described themselves as gay?

2 Were fossils found in Ethiopia in 1994: a) human-like b) dinosaurs c) unknown species?

3 Why did the book *The Bell Curve* (1994) cause controversy?

4 What new grain species was announced to be 20% more productive: a) rice b) wheat c) oats?

5 Osteoporosis made news: is it bone-thinning, hair-loss or abdominal swelling?

6 Which US carmaker was selling Cherokees to Japan?

7 What was the Fulcrum ?

8 Kina hit Fiji in 1993: was it a storm or a disease?

9 Which Central American state was struck by a 1992 earthquake?

10 Which Siberian lake was explored by submersibles in 1990?

11 Which spacecraft mapped Venus from orbit?

12 What in military jargon were CBWs?

13 What were Peacekeepers?

14 Which British bridge lost its number one status?

15 In which European river were pumps installed to add oxygen, to combat pollution?

ANSWERS

1, 1% 2, a) 3, The author argued that intelligence was largely hereditary 4, a) 5, a) 6, Chrysler 7, The MIG-29 jet fighter 8, A storm (a cyclone) 9, Nicaragua 10, Lake Baikal 11, Magellan 12, Chemical and Biological Weapons 13, US land-based missiles 14, The Humber Bridge (for a time world's longest suspension bridge) 15, The Seine

QUIZ 215

POT LUCK

1 Who was the first UK prime minister to address the Irish Parliament?

2 Which new airport opened at Rafah?

3 Which former president was charged with sodomy?

4 To what were Springstein, McCartney and Springfield all inducted in 1999?

5 Of which people was Abdullah Ocalan a leader?

6 Where was the Suzuka International racing circuit?

7 Who won a world title there in 1998?

8 What was HMS *Vengeance?*

9 Whose currency was the ringgit?

10 What nationality was tennis player Mark Philippousis?

11 Which drinks company tried to buy Orangina?

12 And which government said 'no'?

13 Which NBC series won a 5th Emmy in a row in 1998?

14 Which country declared a dead leader 'eternal president'?

15 For what was the Friedrich Kiesler Prize newly awarded?

ANSWERS

1, Tony Blair 2, Gaza International (for Palestine) 3, President Banana of Zimbabwe 4, The Rock and Roll Hall of Fame 5, The Kurds 6, Japan 7, Mikka Hakkinen 8, Britain's 4th Trident submarine 9, Malaysia's 10, Australian 11, Coca-Cola 12, The French 13, *Frasier* 14, North Korea (the leader was Kim Il-sung) 15, Architecture and the Arts

QUIZ 216

1991 WAS A BIG ANNIVERSARY YEAR: IT WAS ...

1 the 15th anniversary of the death of this thriller writer...

2 the 60th anniversary of the death of a famous ballerina...

3 the 50th anniversary of the death of a great Irish writer...

4 30 years since a disastrous US-backed invasion...

5 20 years since the death of Satchmo...

6 the 60th anniversary of the death of a tea merchant turned yachtsman....

7 and 60 years since the death of the inventor of the light bulb...

8 and also of a famous Australian singer...

9 40 years since this American newspaper tycoon died...

10 75 years since the death of the author of White Fang ...

11 50 years since this novelist killed herself...

12 20 years since this group got the vote in the USA...

13 and 325 years since this fire got out of control...

14 50 years after this country entered World War II...

15 and 200 years since the birth of a great English scientist.

ANSWERS

1, Agatha Christie 2, Anna Pavlova 3, James Joyce 4, The Bay of Pigs
5, Louis Armstrong 6, Sir Tommy Lipton 7, Thomas Alva Edison 8, Nellie
Melba 9, William Randolph Hearst 10, Jack London 11, Virginia Woolf
12, 18-year-olds 13, The Great Fire of London 14, The USA
15, Michael Faraday

QUIZ 217

POT LUCK

1 Which show was 'Ab Fab'?

2 Who played Patsy in it?

3 Which TV soap character fell for a North African?

4 What device had Jacques Cousteau (died 1997) helped to invent?

5 In which country did the Kabbah government come under threat from rebels?

6 Which Dutch soccer star was named after his dad's favourite Scottish striker?

7 Who was the Scot?

8 Which French soccer player was banned in 1990 for insulting the national coach?

9 Where was Wang Dan jailed for dissidence?

10 Who was Fat Boy Slim?

11 Which TV personality did he marry?

12 Which Paula set a new US Top 40 record in 1990?

13 How many weeks had she appeared in it?

14 Which rap band recorded 'Ice Ice Baby'?

15 What was Valujet?

ANSWERS

1, *Absolutely Fabulous* 2, Joanna Lumley 3, Deidre in *Coronation Street* 4, The aqualung 5, Sierra Leone 6, Dennis Bergkamp 7, Denis Law (Bergkamp Sr added an 'n') 8, Eric Cantona 9, China 10, A disc jockey 11, Zoe Ball 12, Paula Abdul 13, 68 weeks 14, Vanilla Ice 15, A US airline grounded in 1996

QUIZ 218

WORLD EVENTS

1 What was the CIS?

2 Who founded it in 1991?

3 Which country kept control of the Red army, navy and airforces?

4 Who was Russia's most popular politician in 1991?

5 Where was Bucharest government having problems?

6 In which country was Hyundai HQ based?

7 Which new assembly was called the People's Great Hural?

8 Which state's capital was Monrovia?

9 Which state awarded the King Faisal International Prize?

10 In which country did the Lombard League seek votes?

11 Where was Carl Bildt leader?

12 Where was Bhumibol king?

13 Which Himalayan state adopted democracy in 1991?

14 Which Asian state launched its own communications satellite in 1992?

15 Which country sent troops abroad for the first time since 1945?

ANSWERS

1, Commonwealth of Independent States (a post-Soviet Union grouping of neighbouring states) 2, Russia, Ukraine and Belarus 3, Russia 4, Boris Yeltsin 5, Romania 6, South Korea 7, Mongolia's 8, Liberia 9, Saudi Arabia 10, Italy 11, Sweden 12, Thailand 13, Nepal 14, India 15, Japan

QUIZ 219

SCIENCE & TECHNOLOGY

1 Would a trackball be: a)part of a laptop computer b) a robotic soccer trainer?

2 What do the initials WWW mean to computer buffs?

3 What is an URL?

4 What do the initials CAD stand for in the design world?

5 Which 'Italian' became a well known electronic game character?

6 Modem speeds are measured in bps – standing for what?

7 Are function keys on the top or bottom of a conventional PC keyboard?

8 What exactly is the name CD-ROM short for?

9 Is HTML a software manufacturer or a computer language?

10 What do the initials HTML stand for?

11 Which was the world's biggest manufacturer of computers in the mid-90s?

12 And the largest software company?

13 What in 1993 did a US judge rule was now as 'historical' as documents?

14 Which company introduced the Magic Link voice/e-mail device in 1994?

15 What was a PDA?

ANSWERS

1, a) 2, World Wide Web 3, Uniform Resource Locator 4, Computer Aided Design 5, Mario 6, Bits per second 7, Top 8, Compact Disc Read-Only Memory 9, A computer language 10, Hyper-Text Markup Language 11, IBM 12, Microsoft 13, E-mail 14, Sony 15, Personal Digital Assistant (a pocket-sized computer)

QUIZ 220

WORLD EVENTS

1 Who was Martti Ahtisari?

2 And where was Viktor Chernomyrdin making news?

3 For which government did Strobe Talbot work?

4 Of which country did Ehud Brog (his original name) become leader?

5 What was the Wye Memorandum to do with?

6 What did Amazon.com sell?

7 And where?

8 What did Vincent W Foster do in 1993 that worried the White House?

9 Who was he?

10 Which Turkish politician came back in 1991 after 11 years out of parliament?

11 Whom did Charles Kennedy defeat in a leadership vote?

12 And for what job?

13 Which former Labour leader went to the European Commission?

14 And which ex-governor of Hong Kong joined him?

15 Which Briton left Westminster for NATO?

ANSWERS

1, President of Finland and international negotiator 2, Russia 3, The US (State Department) 4, Israel (as Ehud Barak) 5, Israeli withdrawal from the West Bank 6, Books, videos and CDs 7, On the Internet 8, Killed himself 9, He was a lawyer working for the President 10, Bulent Ecevit 11, Simon Hughes 12, Liberal Democrat party leader 13, Neil Kinnock 14, Chris Patten 15, George (Lord) Robertson

QUIZ 221

SCIENCE & TECHNOLOGY

1 Why did the name Ebola cause concern in the medical world?

2 Where did Norman Thagard fly to in March 95?

3 What was significant about his trip?

4 Which US city had (it said) the world's newest and most advanced airport?

5 What was Troll A?

6 Where were the Petronas Towers?

7 What was their claim to fame?

8 Which country was planning to out-do them?

9 What was the newly discovered chestnut-bellied cotinga?

10 Which big cat was facing extinction in India?

11 Where was the Brent Spar headed, before protests?

12 What was it?

13 Which environmental group led the protests?

14 Which country's transport minister was for a time Brian Mawhinney?

15 What were new roadside checks (1995) designed to reduce?

ANSWERS

1, It is a deadly virus 2, Space, as an astronaut 3, He was the first American to travel by Russian rocket 4, Denver 5, An oil-drilling platform 6, Kuala Lumpur, Malaysia 7, World's tallest buildings, 8, China 9, A bird 10, The tiger 11, To the bottom of the Atlantic Ocean 12, A disused oil-storage platform 13, Greenpeace 14, The UK's 15, Pollution from vehicles

QUIZ 222

POT LUCK

1 At what did Columbus Quest beat Long Beach Stingrays in 1998?
2 Which tycoon bought a Los Angeles baseball team?
3 What were clap skates?
4 Who was Peter Korda?
5 What was the Mach 3, introduced in 98 to make men smoother?
6 What instrument did Pinchas Zukerman play?
7 And to which country did he move to a new job in 1998?
8 Where was Arawa?
9 From which state did people there want to secede?
10 Who agreed to sell missiles to the Greek Cypriots?
11 Where was Gen Lebed a candidate for power?
12 In which continent was the new Suriname wilderness reserve?
13 In which country did an ICE train crash in 1998?
14 In which country was National Elephant Day celebrated?
15 Why did the French whoop it up in Saint-Denis?

ANSWERS

1, Woman's basketball (US championship) 2, Rupert Murdoch 3, New-style skates used at the 98 Winter Olympics 4, A Czech tennis player 5, A new 3-blade shaver from Gillette 6, Violin 7, Canada 8, Capital of Bougainville in the Pacific 9, Papua New Guinea 10, Russia 11, Russia 12, South America 13, Germany 14, Thailand 15, France won the soccer World Cup final

QUIZ 223

SCIENCE & TECHNOLOGY

1 What excited anthropologists about a human bone found in Portugal in 1999?

2 What was the Breitling Orbiter 3?

3 What were found orbiting the star Upsilon Andromedae?

4 What unusual Roman find was dug up in Spitalfields, London in 1999?

5 And what was inside?

6 What was the HST, making news in 1990?

7 Chia Chia became a father in 1990: what was he?

8 Where was the newborn born?

9 In which country were oldest-yet Mayan remains discovered?

10 Which famous ceiling was restored to its original colours?

11 What did ABB manufacture?

12 Which Dutch aircraft maker went bust in 1996?

13 Which country produced the Sukhoi Su-37?

14 And what unusual manoeuvre did it demonstrate at Farnborough?

15 Which new US warplane flew to the UK for a display in 1996, circled, then flew home?

ANSWERS

1, It was a hybrid: half Neanderthal, half modern human 2, The first balloon to fly around the world 3, Three planets 4, A lead coffin 5, The remains of a young woman 6, The Hubble Space Telescope 7, A giant panda 8, Mexico City 9, Guatemala 10, The Sistine Chapel's 11, Electrical equipment 12, Fokker 13, Russia 14, A mid air 'tumble' 15, The Northrop B-2 Stealth bomber

WORLD EVENTS

1 Which European country legalized divorce in 1997?

2 Which country disliked the name Macedonia for a new state?

3 What did 38 Heaven's Gate cult members do in 1997?

4 Who was finally unseated as German Chancellor after four terms?

5 Where did Allen Ginsburg die?

6 And who was he?

7 Which Canadian exchange switched to all-electronic trading?

8 Where did a famous shroud escape fire damage?

9 The desaparecidos were still mourned by protesters; where?

10 What were they?

11 Which TV show in the USA caused controversy when its leading character came out as a lesbian?

12 Which country abolished all trade taxes?

13 Where was Dusan Tadic put on trial?

14 On what charges?

15 In which geographical area were the members of CARICOM?

ANSWERS

1, Ireland 2, Greece 3, Committed mass suicide 4, Helmut Kohl 5, New York 6, An American poet 7, Toronto's stock exchange 8, Turin Cathedral 9, Argentina 10, People who had 'disappeared', presumed arrested or murdered by the government 11, *Ellen* 12, Mongolia 13, The Hague 14, War crimes in the Balkans 15, The Caribbean

QUIZ 225

POT LUCK

1 Who became Sir Paul in 1997?

2 Which sport did Helen Wills Moody (d. 1998) grace?

3 Who was Janet Jagan?

4 And whom did she succeed?

5 For which newly-promoted soccer club did Lee Sharpe play in the Premiership?

6 Who was the actress-wife of American TV writer/producer David E Kelly?

7 And which was his best-known 90s show?

8 How many home runs did Mark McGuire hit in the 1998 baseball season?

9 For which team did he play?

10 Which Keith was usually known as Rupert?

11 Where did the SDP come to power in 1998?

12 And who was its leader?

13 Which TV presenter was shot dead outside her home in 1999?

14 In which city was 1998 World Cup star Zinedine Zidane born?

15 He sang Rudolph the Red Nosed Reindeer, he died in 1998: who was he?

ANSWERS

1, Paul McCartney 2, Tennis 3, First woman president of Guyana 4, Her husband Cheddi Jagan 5, Bradford City 6, Michelle Pfeiffer 7, Ally McBeal 8, 70 9, St Louis Cardinals 10, Murdoch 11, Germany 12, Gerhard Schroder 13, Jill Dando 14, Marseille 15, Gene Autry

QUIZ 226

SPORT

1 Which ice-sport became an Olympic event in 1998?

2 For which Premiership team did Kevin Phillips play soccer?

3 Which famous Australian bowler announced in 1999 he was joining Hampshire?

4 In which sport was use by competitors of the hormone EPO causing problems?

5 Which sport did the Maktoums dominate as owners?

6 Which Brazilian became world showjumping champion in 1998?

7 Who was his famous father, in the same sport?

8 How many goals were scored in normal time in the 1994 World Cup Final?

9 So who won?

10 Which striker left Blackburn Rovers for Chelsea in 1999?

11 Which rhythmic sport featured in the 1998 Goodwill Games?

12 Which sport did Gunde Niemann dominate from 1995?

13 Which sport was new at the 1998 Commonwealth Games ?

14 And who won the men's gold medal in it?

15 What was Dwain Chambers' sport?

ANSWERS

1, Curling 2, Sunderland 3, Shane Warne 4, Cycling 5, Horse racing in Britain 6, Rodrigo Pessoa 7, Nelson Pessoa (also a champion) 8, None 9, Brazil won on penalties against Italy 10, Chris Sutton 11, Artistic gymnastics 12, Women's speed skating 13, Squash 14, Peter Nichol of Scotland 15, Athletics (a British sprinter)

QUIZ 227

POT LUCK

1 Which political party did James Molyneaux lead until 1995?

2 Where was the Million Man March?

3 Which politician who died in 1998 said 'All political careers end in failure'?

4 Where was the city of Mazar el-Sharif overrun?

5 And by whom?

6 What game did the Adelaide Crows play?

7 Where was the world's oldest flower reported in 1998?

8 For what did 700 Anglican bishops gather?

9 Where was the new Stade de France?

10 Which two countries agreed to co-host Euro 2000?

11 Complete this 90s band name: Barenaked -----?

12 Which became the biggest media company in Europe?

13 For which US newspaper did Russell Baker write his last column in 1998?

14 In which TV show did Kenny die in almost every episode?

15 Which US state was the fictional setting for *The Simpsons?*

ANSWERS

1, The Ulster Unionist Party 2, Washington D C 3, Enoch Powell 4, Afghanistan 5, Taliban forces 6, Australian football 7, China 8, The 1998 Lambeth Conference 9, Paris 10, Holland and Belgium 11, Ladies 12, Bertelsmann of Germany 13, *New York Times* 14, *South Park* 15, Texas

QUIZ 228

WHERE WERE THESE LEADERS IN POWER IN 1999?

1 President Arango
2 President Havel
3 Prime minister Jospin
4 Prime minister Bandaranaike
5 Prime minister Mitchell
6 President Karimov
7 Prime minister Kok
8 President Kim Dae Jung
9 President Cardoso
10 President Mejdani
11 President Meri
12 Prime minister Vajpayee
13 President McAleese
14 Prime minister Obuchi
15 President Muluzi

ANSWERS

1, Colombia 2, Czech Republic 3, France 4, Sri Lanka 5, Grenada 6, Uzbekistan 7, Holland 8, South Korea 9, Brazil 10, Albania 11, Estonia 12, India 13, Ireland 14, Japan 15, Malawi

QUIZ 229

POT LUCK

1 Which TV show opened with the words 'The truth is out there'?

2 Where was the series filmed: a) Vancouver b) Miami c) Sydney?

3 Who was Michael Flatley?

4 What was the FDA in the United States?

5 What nationality was golfer Jesper Parnevik?

6 Which new state's capital was Yerevan?

7 Which language dominated the Internet?

8 Which crime-fighting organization did Louis Freeh head?

9 What kind of craft was the *Nimitz?*

10 What do the initials IATA stand for?

11 What sport did Mary Pierce play?

12 What cult did David Koresh lead?

13 What was the title of the sequel to *Jurassic Park?*

14 Who was Cathy Freeman?

15 What did Rosie O'Donnell do on TV?

ANSWERS

1, *The X-Files* 2, a) 3, The original star of *Riverdance* 4, The Food and Drink Administration 5, Swedish 6, Armenia 7, English 8, The FBI 9, A US aircraft carrier 10, International Air Transport Association 11, Tennis 12, The Branch Davidians 13, *The Lost World* 14, An Australian athlete 15, She hosted an American chat/celebrity show

QUIZ 230

WORLD EVENTS

THE YEAR WAS 1997

1 Who became America's first woman Secretary of State?

2 Who was the youngest woman to win a Grand Slam tennis title (1997)

3 Twins were born in 1997 a record time apart: how long?

4 Where was Marc Detroux on trial for sex crimes?

5 Where was Rene Preval president?

6 In what game was a perfect 900 series bowled?

7 Who was charged with the deaths of Nicole Brown Simpson and Ron Goldman?

8 Where did unemployment rates soar to 1930s levels?

9 Who was Heidi Fleiss?

10 How did a nurse in Massachusetts win a record million dollars?

11 What topped 7000 for the first time in 1997?

12 In which sport was Tara Lipinski a champion at 14?

13 What kind of new flower was 'Blackjack'?

14 On which New York landmark did a terrorist start shooting?

15 From whom did Sister Nirmala take over?

ANSWERS

1, Madeleine Albright 2, Martina Hingis (aged 16) 3, 92 days 4, Belgium 5, Haiti 6, Ten pin bowling 7, O J Simpson 8, Germany 9, She was the 'madam' in the 'Hollywood madam' trial 10, Playing Bingo 11, The Dow Jones industrial average 12, Ice skating 13, A dark tulip 14, The Empire State Building 15, Mother Teresa, as head of the Missionaries of Charity

QUIZ 231

POT LUCK

1 For which show was TV-creator Chris Carter best known?

2 Who starred in the animated film *A Grand Day Out?*

3 Which sheep appeared on thousands of kids' backpacks?

4 Which popular entertainer who had once set a tap-dancing record died in 1994?

5 Which mac-wearing 70s detective returned to the screen in 1991?

6 Which comic hosted *Small Talk* (1994)?

7 In which children's TV series did the Pevensies feature?

8 Who played a chef called Gareth Blackstock in a TV series?

9 Show's title?

10 What were the two team-colours in *Ready Steady Cook?*

11 Which TV cook had Norwich City FC dear to her heart?

12 Who directed the film *True Lies?*

13 And which ship did he steer to Oscar triumphs?

14 Which TV series spawned a movie sub-titled *Fight the Future?*

15 Which William Rice Burroughs hero was 'Disneyfied'?

ANSWERS

1, *The X-Files* 2, Wallace and Gromit 3, Sean the Sheep 4, Roy Castle 5, Columbo 6, Ronnie Corbett 7, *The Chronicles of Narnia* 8, Lenny Henry 8, *Chef* 10, Green Peppers, Red Tomatoes 11, Delia Smith 12, James Cameron 13, *Titanic* 14, *The X-Files* 15, *Tarzan*

QUIZ 232

SPORT

SOCCER

Name 1) country and 2) the sport of these stars

1 Dan Luger?
2 And what sport did he play?
3 Laurent Blanc?
4 Sport?
5 Justin Langer?
6 Sport?
7 Allan Donald?
8 Sport?
9 Magnus Norman?
10 Sport?
11 Emile Heskey?
12 Sport?
13 Patrick Kluivert?
14 Sport?
15 And what nationality was top athlete Haile Gebrselassie?

ANSWERS

1, England 2, Rugby 3, France 4, Soccer 5, Australia 6, Cricket 7, South Africa 8, Cricket 9, Sweden 10, Tennis 11, England 12, Soccer 13, Holland 14, Soccer 15, Ethiopian

WORLD EVENTS

IT WAS 1997

1 Which country owned the tanker Nakhodka?

2 And where was it wrecked?

3 Who was re-elected Speaker in the US House of Representatives?

4 Where was Bangui, scene of a mutiny?

5 What was NeXT?

6 And which company planned a deal with it?

7 Where did the Grimaldis mark 700 years of rule?

8 Where was Lake Nasser providing more water for desert farmers?

9 Which group controlled the army in Burundi: Tutsi or Hutu?

10 Which American spacecraft docked with a Russian?

11 Which tycoon launched a Chinese internet service?

12 Where did Borge Osland travel and how?

13 Where was Skanderbeg Square?

14 Who was inaugurated for his second term as president despite 'the Monica affair'?

15 A survivor of a 1912 sinking died, aged 100: which disaster had she survived?

ANSWERS

1, Russia 2, Off Japan 3, Central African Republic 4, Newt Gingrich 5, A software company 6, Apple Computer Inc. 7, Monaco 8, Egypt 9, Tutsi 10, The shuttle *Atlantis* with *Mir* 11, Rupert Murdoch 12, Across Antarctica on skis 13, Tirane, in Albania 14, Bill Clinton 15, The sinking of the Titanic

QUIZ 234

POT LUCK

1 What was *Destriero?*

2 And what did it do in 58 hours in 1992?

3 Who was dragged to the Chair by two MPs in 1992?

4 And who in that year became Yorkshire's first overseas cricketer?

5 Who succeeded Sir Patrick Walker in a top-secret job?

6 Which 3-wheeler did a ton on the M20?

7 And which TV character drove one in a comedy series?

8 Title of the series?

9 What was the name of Britain's first Trident submarine?

10 What did Masters and Johnson study together no more after 1992?

11 What honour did Dirk Frimout achieve?

12 Was Nick Gillingham a swimmer, a rower or a boxer?

13 Which famous London police station closed for rebuilding?

14 What was the world's first genetically-engineered food (1992)?

15 Which country welcomed the hula hoop as a keep-fit aid?

ANSWERS

1, An Italian speedboat 2, It crossed the Atlantic 3, The new Speaker, Betty Boothroyd 4, Sachin Tendulkar 5, Stella Rimington (head of MI-5) 6, A Reliant Robin 7, Del Boy 8, *Only Fools And Horses* 9, HMS *Vanguard* 10, Sex (they divorced in 1992) 11, First Belgian in space 12, A swimmer 13, Bow Street 14, A tomato 15, China

QUIZ 235

SCIENCE & TECHNOLOGY

1 1997 XF11 was headed toward us: what was it?

2 What did Lunar Prospector detect?

3 What was the drug Relenza meant to treat?

4 Of which childhood disease were there only 100 cases in the USA in 1998?

5 What was Archaefrutus?

6 What was the German-built ABRIXAS?

7 What crashed into the Moon in 1999?

8 In computer jargon, what is an OS?

9 In which branch of science did Linus Torvalds rise to fame and wealth?

10 Where was he born (country)?

11 Which group of people got excited about the proof of the Taniyama-Shimura Conjecture?

12 What on earth was a Higgs boson?

13 Where did Zarya meet Unity in 1999?

14 And of what were they the first stage?

15 What kind of instrument was the Keck II 10-metre?

ANSWERS

1, An asteroid 2, Water on the Moon 3, Types of the influenza virus 4, Measles 5, A newly discovered fossil plant 6, An X-ray satellite for astronomy 7, Lunar Prospector 8, OS = Operating System 9, Computer science 10, Finland 11, Mathematicians 12, A hypothetical subatomic particle 13, In space 14, The International Space Station 15, A telescope

QUIZ 236

SPORT

1 Which teenage French star left Arsenal for Real Madrid in 1999?

2 Who left Old Trafford to manage Blackburn Rovers?

3 For which country did Nasser Hussain play cricket?

4 Which Yorkshire wicket-keeper died in January 1998?

5 Which sport made its Olympic debut at the 1998 Winter Olympics?

6 Who overhauled Richie Benaud as Australia's most succesful leg-spinner?

7 Which sport's governing body was the UCI?

8 What medical check did it introduce in 1997?

9 Which African horses were back on the track?

10 Why had they been banned since the 1970s?

11 In which sport did Labegorce beat Black Bears in 1997?

12 Who became Chelsea's first Italian manager?

13 Who signed Rivaldo to replace Ronaldo?

14 Which Welsh soccer player topped European goal-scoring lists with 42 goals in 96-97?

15 Was golfer Justin Leonard a) Australian b) British c) American?

ANSWERS

1, Nicolas Anelka 2, Brian Kidd 3, Essex 4, David Bairstow
5, Snowboarding 6, Shane Warne 7, Cycling 8, Random blood tests
9, South African race horses 10, Because of African horse sickness
11, Polo 12, Gianluca Vialli 13, Barcelona 14, Tony Bird of Barry Town
15, c)

QUIZ 237

POT LUCK

1 Who were Serena and Venus?

2 To whom was the X-Prize on offer?

3 Which MP refused to sit in the royal box for the1998 Cup Final?

4 At the time he was minister for...what?

5 Of which reduced state was Montenegro part?

6 Who was Violet Lewis's famous son?

7 What beat Gary Kasparov in 1997?

8 What record did Senator Strom Thurmond break?

9 Which pioneer aviator's last Pacific flight was recreated?

10 Which country decided to close its main Antarctic base to save money?

11 By what name was the Antoinette Perry Award better known?

12 Who was Claudia Kennedy and why had she three stars?

13 Where did Soufriere Hills volcano erupt?

14 Neville Crump, who died in 1997, was a leading figure in which sport?

15 Whose divorce became final in August 1996?

ANSWERS

1, The tennis-playing Williams sisters 2, First amateur team to send people into space 3, Tony Banks 4, Sport 5, Yugoslavia 6, Boxer Lennox Lewis 7, A computer called Deep Blue beat him at chess 8, He became the longest-serving US senator 9, Amelia Earhart's 10, Russia 11, Tony Award 12, The first woman 3-star general in the US Army 13, Montserrat 14, Horse racing 15, The Prince and Princess of Wales

QUIZ 238

SCIENCE & TECHNOLOGY

1 Some scientists claimed to have discovered a sixth and 'top' – what?

2 In space science what was the SRL?

3 Which telescope did astronauts repair in 1993?

4 Which Asian volcano spewed dirt into the atmosphere in 1991?

5 From which planet were pictures of Maat Mons beamed to Earth?

6 And what is Maat Mons?

7 Which US state was hard hit by drought as the 90s began?

8 Which country consumed the most soft drinks per head in 1990?

9 Which company claimed to be the world's largest seller of soft drinks?

10 What are fullerenes?

11 After whom are they named?

12 Which famous zoo survived a closure-scare in 1991?

13 Which Australian-born animal was the first of its species to be born in captivity since the 1940s?

14 TB was on the increase: TB stands for-------?

15 How did European doctors recommend babies should be placed to sleep?

ANSWERS

1, Quark 2, Space Radar Laboratory 3, Hubble 4, Mt Pinatubo (Philippines) 5, Venus 6, The 2nd highest mountain on Venus 7, California 8, The USA 9, Coca-Cola 10, Ball-shaped carbon molecules 11, Architect/engineer Buckminster Fuller 12, London Zoo 13, A duckbilled platypus 14, Tuberculosis 15, On their backs

QUIZ 239

POT LUCK

1991

1 Whose long jump record was at last broken?

2 Which world leader collapsed while jogging?

3 Who found none of the phones in his holiday home worked?

4 What did Terry Anderson and Jackie Mann have in common?

5 Which historic walled city in Yugoslavia was under siege?

6 Who was the first Western statesman to address Mongolia's parliament?

7 Who disappeared from the *Lady Ghislaine?*

8 Who were freed at the Old Bailey 17 years after conviction?

9 What happened to Flt Lt John Peters?

10 Who decided not to marry Keifer Sutherland?

11 Who called herself a 'fun mum'?

12 Which 'biscuits' were ruled to be cakes in a VAT case?

13 What was BCCI?

14 What kind of vessel was the *Haven?*

15 And what happened to it?

ANSWERS

1, Bob Beamon's (1968) 2, George Bush 3, Mikhail Gorbachev 4, Both were released Middle East hostages 5, Dubrovnik 6, US Secretary of State James Baker 7, Robert Maxwell 8, The Birmingham 6 9, He was captured by the Iraqis during the Gulf War 10, Julia Roberts 11, The Duchess of York 12, Jaffa cakes 13, A bank shut down for fraud 14, An oil tanker 15, It exploded in the Bay of Genoa

QUIZ 240

WORLD EVENTS

THE UNITED KINGDOM IN 1999

1 Where did Plaid Cymru hope for more votes?

2 Into what did the Macpherson Inquiry inquire?

3 Whose 1993 murder had led to this inquiry?

4 Who became first minister-elect in Northern Ireland?

5 Who replaced Mo Mowlam there?

6 What was Michael Meacher's ministry?

7 Who got rid of mortgage interest relief?

8 In what military action did RAF planes take part?

9 Which two parties won first-ever Euro-Parliament seats?

10 What was the full name of the UKIP?

11 Which former Tory ministers backed a pro-euro campaign?

12 What did the EC say farmers could sell abroad again?

13 But which European countries were slow to respond?

14 Which Chilean remained the subject of legal wrangling?

15 How did he come to be in the UK?

ANSWERS

1, Wales 2, Alleged 'institutional racism' in the police 3, The murder of Stephen Lawrence 4, David Trimble 5, Peter Mandelson 6, Environment 7, Chancellor Gordon Brown 8, The NATO bombing of Yugoslav targets in and around Kosovo 9, The Greens and UKIP 10, United Kingdom Independence Party 11, Michael Heseltine and Kenneth Clarke 12, British beef 13, France and Germany 14, General Pinochet 15, He'd been arrested in 1998 (but eventually returned to Chile)

QUIZ 241

SPORT

1 Which English Premier League side did Steve Bruce captain?

2 For which club did Anders Limpar play?

3 Whom did Paul Gascoigne foul in the 1991 Cup Final, (and receive a bad injury in so doing)?

4 Which team were Gascoigne's opponents?

5 And whose own goal decided the match?

6 For whom did Mark Wright play in World Cup 90?

7 Which Italian club did David Platt join when he first moved to Italy?

8 Who was Leeds manager in 1992?

9 Who replaced Ardiles as boss of Newcastle?

10 What year did the Premier League start?

11 Which player got into trouble for a "Hard Men" video?

12 Which colourful manager's career ended on a low when Nottingham Forest were relegated?

13 Which club said goodbye to Terry?

14 And hello to Teddy (and who was he)?

15 With which club did the same Teddy later win a European medal?

ANSWERS

1, Manchester United 2, Arsenal 3, Gary Charles 4, Nottingham Forest 5, Des Walker 6, England 7, Bari 8, Howard Wilkinson 9, Kevin Keegan 10, 1993 11, Vinnie Jones 12, Brian Clough 13, Tottenham Hotspur sacked Terry Venables 14, And signed Teddy Sheringham 15, Manchester United

QUIZ 242

POT LUCK

1 Which actress wore a dress held together by safety pins?
2 At which film's premiere?
3 And who designed the dress?
4 Who was the actress's actor-boyfriend?
5 And which football team did he support?
6 Which store-owner acquired this club?
7 And which ex-England striker did he appoint as new club boss?
8 Which team lured that coach away?
9 And which stadium (in which it played) was to be redeveloped?
10 Which new building in the same city featured the Body Zone?
11 And who was the building's architect?
12 Which Tube line was extended to carry in visitors?
13 Which UK minister had responsibility for railways in 1999?
14 Which make of car did he like to drive?
15 And to whom was he officially deputy?

ANSWERS

1, Elizabeth Hurley 2, *Four Weddings and a Funeral* 3, Versace 4, Hugh Grant 5, Fulham 6, Mohammed Al-Fayed 7, Kevin Keegan 8, The England team 9, Wembley Stadium 10, The Millennium Dome 11, Richard Rodgers 12, The Jubilee Line 13, John Prescott 14, Jaguar 15, The Prime Minister

QUIZ 243

SPORT

1 Which cricket batsman set a new Test record of 10,122 runs in 1993?

2 Whose record did he overhaul?

3 Which cricketer scored a world record 375 in 1994?

4 Against whom?

5 And where was the match?

6 Which English batsman scored a total of 456 in one 1990 Test?

7 What country were England playing?

8 And where?

9 What were his two scores?

10 Which brothers set a national batting record in 1994-95 against Pakistan?

11 For which country were they playing?

12 Which all-rounder overhauled the record Test wicket total by a bowler in 1994?

13 Who had held the old record?

14 Which landmark had this player (qu. 13) passed in 1990?

15 Which English bowler took a wicket with his first Test match ball in 1991?

ANSWERS

1, Allan Border 2, Suril Gavaskar 3, Brian Lara 4, England 5, Antigua 6, Graham Gooch 7, India 8, Lord's 9, 333 and 123 10, Grant and Andy Flower 11, Zimbabwe 12, Kapil Dev 13, Richard Hadlee 14, First bowler to take 400 Test wickets 15, Richard Illingworth

QUIZ 244

WORLD EVENTS

1999 WAS THE YEAR

1 Where was the Salam newspaper closed down?

2 Where was Habibie president?

3 Whose daughter was Megawati?

4 And what was she after?

5 Who headed UNSCOM in Iraq?

6 And what were the 'WMDs' it was looking for?

7 Where was Bertie Ahern prime minister?

8 What was the popular name for the Northern Ireland peace agreement?

9 Who resigned as Likud leader after losing an election?

10 Which country provided 11 air bases for the NATO attacks on Yugoslavia?

11 Whose wife was Queen Rania?

12 Which government closed the Baikonur space centre?

13 Which country had been paying to use it?

14 Which continent was worst affected by AIDS?

15 Where was prime minister Nawaz Sharif deposed?

ANSWERS

1, Iran 2, Indonesia 3, Former president Sukarno's 4, The Indonesian presidency 5, Richard Butler 6, Weapons of Mass Destruction 7, Ireland 8, The Good Friday Agreement 9, Benjamin Netanyahu 10, Italy 11, Jordan's King Abdullah 12, Kazakstan 13, Russia 14, Africa 15, Pakistan

QUIZ 245

SPORT

1 Which country won most medals at the 98 Commonwealth Games?

2 In which sport did this country take 23 gold medals?

3 For which team did Mika Hakkinen drive in 1998?

4 Which sport did his fellow-Finn Tommi Makinen dominate?

5 What is the world's oldest car race, won in 1998 by Eddie Cheever?

6 In what sport did a 1961 record held by Roger Maris fall?

7 Which record was it?

8 And who set the new high mark?

9 For whom did Michael Jordan play basketball?

10 In which sport did a record 14 nations compete at Preston in 1998?

11 For whom were Ambrose and Walsh still going strong?

12 What 1998 classic did High-Rise win in England?

13 Which organisation chose 'Sepp' Blatter to lead it?

14 Which football club did BSkyB try to buy in 1998?

15 Which British club won the Cup-Winners' Cup 97-98?

ANSWERS

1, Australia 2, Swimming 3, Mclaren-Mercedes 4, Rally driving 5, The Indianapolis 500 6, Baseball 7, Number of home runs in a US season (61) 8, Mark McGuire (70) 9, Chicago Bulls 10, Snooker 11, The West Indies 12, The Derby 13, FIFA 14, Manchester United 15, Chelsea

QUIZ 246

POT LUCK

1 Harold Larwood died in 1996; what game had he played?

2 Who was Darcy Bussell?

3 Where was Sonia Gandhi born?

4 In which country had she become a major political figure?

5 Who was Michael Duane Johnson?

6 Who played Saffron on TV in a popular series?

7 What was its title?

8 And who played her mother Edina?

9 In which TV series did Kevin Whately play a doctor?

10 In which soap did 'Beth Jordache' feature?

11 Which of the *Star Trek* sequels was set in the 24th century?

12 Which character did Pat St Clement play in a TV soap?

13 In whose government did Clare Short become a minister?

14 With which TV show was Richard Madeley primarily associated?

15 Was Paula Radcliffe a runner, a singer or a model?

ANSWERS

1, Cricket 2, A ballet dancer 3, Italy 4, India 5, US runner, one of the great athletes of the 90s 6, Julia Sawalha 7, *Absolutely Fabulous* 8, Jennifer Saunders 9, *Peak Practice* 10, *Brookside* 11, *StarTrek Voyager* 12, Pat Wicks/Butcher in *EastEnders* 13, Labour government, UK 14, *This Morning* 15 She was a British runner

QUIZ 247

SPORT

1 In which sport was Scotland's David Millar a young hopeful?

2 Which national side did Dino Zoff coach?

3 Who was manager of Tottenham Hotspur when the 90s ended?

4 In which sport was Sir Michael Stoute prominent?

5 What game did the Williams sisters play?

6 What did Henry Paul play for Bradford?

7 What sport did the Thames Valley club play in the UK?

8 With which Rrugby League club did Dennis Betts make his name in the 90s?

9 For which country did Emile Mpenza play soccer?

10 What team did Bernard Gallacher captain?

11 In what event did Trine Hattestad win world titles?

12 What national soccer tream did Erich Ribbeck coach in 1999?

13 Who was Liverpool's first French coach?

14 Who were Greg and Tim?

15 And in what sport did Mal Washington make a fleeting headline appearance in the 90s?

ANSWERS

1, Cycling 2, Italy (soccer) 3, George Graham 4, Horse racing 5, Tennis 6, Rugby League 7, Basketball 8, Wigan 9, Belgium 10, Britain and Europe Ryder Cup team (golf) 11, Javelin throwing 12, Germany 13, Gerard Houllier 14, Rusedski and Henman (tennis) 15, Tennis

QUIZ 248

POT LUCK

1 What were 75% of all Britons doing in 1995?

2 With whom did Princess Diana admit adultery?

3 What bestseller chronicled the diary of a 30-something chain-smoker?

4 And who wrote it?

5 What was *Arena Homme Plus?*

6 Which UK newspaper did Charles Moore edit?

7 Were Hizbullah a group active in a) South America b) Southeast Asia c) The Middle East?

8 For what title was Viswanathan Anand a challenger?

9 Where did people speak Kazak?

10 If the Broncos were from Denver, where did the Vikings play?

11 Which British team also used the name Broncos?

12 And which Yorkshire team became the Bulls?

13 Which cartoon TV series did Matt Groening create?

14 Which country drank the most wine per head (1997 figures)?

15 And which farmed the most fish?

ANSWERS

1, Buying lottery tickets or scratch cards 2, James Hewitt 3, *Bridget Jones's Diary* 4, Helen Fielding 5, A men's magazine 6, *The Daily Telegraph* 7, c) The Middle East 8, World Chess Champion 9, Kazakstan 10, Minnesota 11, London's Rugby League club 12, Bradford Rugby League club 13, *The Simpsons* 14, Portugal 15, China

QUIZ 249

HOW UP TO DATE ARE YOU WITH WORLD CURRENCIES? TRY THESE FROM 1999!

1 Afghani
2 Kwanza
3 Boliviano
4 Colon
5 Moldovan leu
6 Tugrik
7 Rand
8 Manat
9 Pa'anga
10 Escudo
11 Zloty
12 Kip
13 Baht
14 Cedi
15 Kroon

ANSWERS

1,Afghanistan 2,Angola 3,Bolivia 4,El Salvador 4,Moldova 6,Mongolia
7,South Africa 8,Turkmenistan 9,Tonga 10,Portugal 11,Poland
12,Laos 13,Thailand 14,Ghana 15,Estonia

QUIZ 250

SPORT

SOCCER

For which country was each of these players capped?

1 Martin Keown?
2 Dietmar Hamann?
3 Luis Figo?
4 Dan Petrescu?
5 Jim Leighton?
6 Niall Quinn?
7 Henrik Larsson?
8 Thierry Henry?
9 Paolo Maldini?
10 Jaap Stam?
11 Gilles de Bilde?
12 Gianfranco Zola?
13 Francesco Hierro?
14 Savo Milosevic?
15 Steffen Iversen?

ANSWERS

1, England 2, Liverpool 3, Portugal 4, Romania 5, Scotland 6, Irish
Republic 7, Sweden 8, Belgium 9, Italy 10, Holland 11, Belgium 12, Italy
13, Spain 14, Yugoslavia 15, Norway

QUIZ 251

POT LUCK

1 Which pop star didn't tour Canada in 1996 because he was 'house hunting'?

2 Name his band's late-90s album: *Standing On*------?

3 Which TV item was no longer 'At Ten'?

4 Who hosted the *Supermarket Sweep?*

5 Which radio soap had its first gay publican?

6 Which veteran jazz man still 'hadn't a clue' on radio?

7 Which BBC network came new to medium wave in the UK?

8 And who was the Danny who sometimes tackled football?

9 Which French musical was a smash in Paris (but later was panned in London)?

10 Disney made a film from the same Hugo novel. Title?

11 A London based show from a Hugo novel was still going strong. Which?

12 Which singer was celebrated in the musical *Buddy?*

13 And which group in *Mamma Mia?*

14 From which country did the 1992 musical *Which Witch* come to London?

15 Which veteran pop singer appeared in a musical version of *Wuthering Heights?*

ANSWERS

1, Liam Gallagher 2, *The Shoulders of Giants* 3, ITN news 4, Dale Winton 5, *The Archers* 6, Humphrey Lyttelton (who presented BBC Radio's *I'm Sorry I Haven't A Clue*) 7, Radio Five Live 8, Danny Baker 9, Notre-Dame de Paris 10, *The Hunchback of Notre Dame* 11, *Les Miserables* 12, Buddy Holly 13, ABBA 14, Norway 15, Cliff Richard

QUIZ 252

SPORT

RUGBY UNION

1 For which national side did Jonathan Callard play?

2 Which player was Wales's star goal-kicker of the decade?

3 Which team beat England in the 1991 World Cup?

4 Can you remember the score?

5 Which national team scored its first-ever win in France in 1992?

6 For which country did Eric Elwood play?

7 Which English club side did Jeremy Guscott play for?

8 Did Paul Thornburn play for Wales, Australia or England?

9 What position did both Jonathon Callard and Simon Hodgekinson play?

10 Which former England centre became England coach?

11 Which RAF pilot jetted down the wing for England?

12 And which other member of his family was also capped for England?

13 For what national team did Robert Howley play?

14 Was Keith Wood capped for Ireland or England?

15 Who was 'Deano'?

ANSWERS

1, England 2, Neil Jenkins 3, Australia 4, 12-6 5, Argentina 6, Ireland 7, Bath 8, Wales 9, Full-back 10, Clive Woodward 11, Rory Underwood 12, Brother Tony Underwood 13, Wales 14, Ireland 15, Dean Richards (Leicester and England)

QUIZ 253

POT LUCK

1 Which actor, who died in 1997, said in a memorable film 'Help me, Clarence. I wanna live again'?

2 By what nickname was R. W. Rowland usually known?

3 What was Hale-Bopp?

4 What did 39 Heaven's Gate believers do on seeing it?

5 What was a metre long and spotted in London's Regent Canal?

6 A 90s curiosity: what unusual object was found inside an eating apple: a) a fossilized beetle b) a gold ring c) a false tooth?

7 Her husband described this lady, who died in 1997, as 'the greatest courtesan of the century'. Who was she?

8 Where did Oscar Romero, Janani Luwum and Martin Luther King stand side by side?

9 Who were the world's top 'chocaholics' according to a 90s survey?

10 How did Liz Buttle make news in 1996?

11 What did three Yemenis say they owned, and in 1997 they sued NASA for going there?

12 Which animals in New Zealand were given experimental 'woolovers' to keep them warm?

13 And which animals 'invaded' a Kenyan hospital: a) locusts b) elephants c) baboons ?

14 Which unloved English counties were deleted from the map?

15 And which 'club' did Cameroon join in 1995?

ANSWERS

1, James Stewart in *It's A Wonderful Life* (1946) 2, 'Tiny' 3, A comet seen in 1997 4, They killed themselves 5, A reptile possibly a crocodile 6, b) 7, Pamela Harriman 8, On the west front of Westminster Abbey (they were new statues) 9, The British 10 Gave birth, allegedly aged 61 11, The planet Mars 12, Lambs 13, Baboons 14, Cleveland, Avon and Humberside 15, The Commonwealth

QUIZ 254

SCIENCE & TECHNOLOGY

1 Who was the designer of the He-178, who died in 1998?

2 What was the He-178?

3 After Dolly, what or who was Polly?

4 Whose 'lost tomb' was reported found in the Egyptian desert?

5 And whose Lyceum was discovered in Greece?

6 On what did Bruce Bursford travel at 207.9mph in 1995?

7 Which country was estimated (1996) to have the most landmines?

8 What did the initials BSE stand for ?

9 What Nobel Prize had Sir Geoffrey Wilkinson (died1996) shared in 1973?

10 What was the CBD a convention about?

11 Works from ancient Bagram went on show: where was Bagram?

12 What kind of new animal was the Panay cloudrunner?

13 And where was it discovered in 1996?

14 Which small Internet company fought a giant in the so-called 'browser wars'?

15 And what was the giant's new weapon?

ANSWERS

1, Hans von Ohain 2, The world's first jet plane 3, The first cloned sheep with human genes 4, Alexander the Great's 5, Aristotle's 6, A bicycle 7, Egypt 8, Bovine spongiform encephalopathy 9, Chemistry 10, CBD = Convention on Biological Diversity 11, The Kushan Empire, 1st century AD 12, A squirrel-like mammal 13, Panay island in the Philippines 14, Netscape 15, Microsoft's Internet Explorer

QUIZ 255

SPORT

1 Which England player moved from Manchester to Milan in 1995?

2 Who became Aston Villa's biggest-ever 'sale' in 1998?

3 Which club did the Villa player join?

4 Which manager took Manchester City up from Div 2 to Div I in 1999?

5 Who managed Manchester City 1990-93, and later enjoyed success with Sunderland?

6 Which ex-England skipper moved to Middlesborough in 1994?

7 Which club paid £15 million for a centre-forward in 1996?

8 And who was he?

9 Which player moved to Anfield in 1995, to Villa in 1997, and to Leicester in 1999?

10 Who quit suddenly as Liverpool's manager in 1991?

11 Who managed Chelsea from 1993-96?

12 And who followed him?

13 Which club briefly appointed Dr Josef Venglos manager in 1990?

14 And who then took over (until 1994)?

15 Which was the most expensive player of the 90s?

ANSWERS

1, Paul Ince 2, Dwight Yorke 3, Manchester United 4, Joe Royle 5, Peter Reid 6, Bryan Robson 7, Newcastle United 8, Alan Shearer 9, Stan Collymore 10, Kenny Dalglish 11, Glenn Hoddle 12, Ruud Gullit 13, Aston Villa 14, Ron Atkinson 15, Christian Vieri

SPORT

WHAT WAS THEIR SPORT?

1 Ray Stevens (Britain)?

2 Jennifer Capriati (USA)?

3 Nicola Fairbrother (Britain)?

4 Torsten May (Germany)?

5 Heike Dreschler (Germany)?

6 Uwe-Jens Mey (Germany)?

7 Oksane Baiul (Ulkraine)?

8 Marc Rosset (Switzerland)?

9 David Sole (Scotland)?

10 Austin Healey (England)?

11 David Coulthard (Scotland)?

12 Carl Lewis (USA)?

13 Mary Pierce (France)?

14 Zinedine Zidane (France)?

15 Evander Holyfield (USA)?

ANSWERS

1,Judo 2,Tennis 3,Judo 4,Boxing 5,Long jump 6,Speed skating
7,Figure skating 8,Tennis 9,Rugby 10,Rugby 11,Motor racing
12,Athletics 13,Tennis 14,Soccer 15,Boxing

QUIZ 257

POT LUCK

1 In 1998, who was the oldest resident of Powderham Castle, aged 150+ years?

2 Where was the Eredo monument being explored?

3 What cost over £800 in 1999 compared with £1 in 1899?

4 Which parliament's new home opened in Brussels in 1997?

5 And where was its second home, also new (1999)?

6 Who was the new Earl of Wessex?

7 And on which finger did he wear his wedding ring (unusually)?

8 Which ex-child star died in 1999 after a long struggle against anorexia?

9 Where was a Imperial Roman circus recreated in Asia?

10 And what part of the show aroused animal-lovers to protest?

11 What new invention contained a speck of glowing gallium nitride?

12 This 'Singing the Blues' star died in 1999. Who was he?

13 What did 52% of adults say they would do, if they could get away with it?

14 Who was Britain's Chief Rabbi in 1999?

15 What was straightened by 0.8 of an inch?

ANSWERS

1, Timothy, a tortoise 2, Nigeria 3, A season ticket for Arsenal FC 4, The European Parliament's 5, Strasbourg 6, Prince Edward 7, The little finger of the left hand 8, Lena Zavaroni 9, China 10, Live calves were reportedly fed to lions 11, An everlasting light bulb 12, Guy Mitchell 13, Claim they'd cooked a ready meal 14, Jonathan Sacks 15 The Leaning Tower of Pisa

QUIZ 258

POT LUCK

1 Who had declared 'Loonyism will go on for ever'?

2 Which ancient writing material was to be phased out of Parliamentary Acts?

3 Where was KFOR deployed in 1999?

4 And who were the KLA?

5 Who were Gremlin and Robbie, who retired in 1999?

6 Whose kissing was rated '11 out of 10'?

7 By whom?

8 And which film did this all refer to?

9 Who was described as a 'flatulent 62-year-old windbag'?

10 And who delivered the rebuke?

11 Which lost climber's body was discovered on Mt Everest?

12 When had he last been seen alive?

13 Of whom did Sir Bobby Charlton say 'he gave us our proudest moment'?

14 What did 'triboluminescence' do to a baby's nappy in April 1999?

15 Who was Britain's Chief Schools Inspector?

ANSWERS

1, Screaming Lord Sutch 2, Vellum (no longer to be used for copies of legislation) 3, Kosovo 4, The Kosovo Liberation Army 5, Britain's last pit ponies 6, Sean Connery's 7, Catherine Zeta Jones 8, *Entrapment* 9, Michael Caine 10, Richard Harris 13, Sir Alf Ramsey 14, The nappy glowed green, without apparent harm to the wearer 15, Chris Woodhead

QUIZ 259

SPORT

SOCCER

1 For which country did Oliver Kahn keep goal?

2 Who scored their winning 'golden goal' in Euro 96?

3 Who were the only brothers to play for England in the 1990s?

4 Who were the last brothers to be capped together for England?

5 For whom did Paul Ince win Cup and League medals in 1994?

6 Which international left Liverpool for Spain in 1999?

7 Who captained Germany in the 1990 World Cup finals?

8 Which English club did Romanian striker Vlorel Moldovan join in 1998, before moving to Turkey?

9 For which club did his fellow Romanian Dan Petrescu play in England before joining Chelsea in 1995?

10 Which England forward moved from Bari to Juuentus in 1992?

11 Which England player moved to Marseille from Rangers in 1991?

12 Which Yorkshire club had Danny Wilson in charge at the start of the 1999-2000 season?

13 For which Premiership side did Harry Kewell play?

14 To which British club did Bobby Robson return to British management?

15 Which London club did Alan Curbishley manage?

ANSWERS

1, Germany 2, Oliver Bierhoff 3, The Nevilles, Gary and Phil 4, The Charltons, Jack and Bobby (1970) 5, Manchester United 6, Steve McManaman 7, Lothar Matthaus 8, Coventry City 9, Sheffield Wednesday 10, David Platt 11, Trevor Steven 12, Sheffield Wednesday 13, Leeds United 14, Newcastle United 15, Charlton Athletic

QUIZ 260

SCIENCE & TECHNOLOGY

1 What did scientists find made chicks less stressed?

2 Which predators were returned to Yellowstone National Park?

3 Which record-breaking car turned up beneath a New Zealand rubbish dump?

4 Which small furry animals had to be moved from the path of the Channel Tunnel rail link in Kent?

5 What kind of 'implants' were criticised by US medical experts?

6 What was alleged to have been dumped in the Karas and Barents seas?

7 Where was the new Alamillo Bridge (1992)?

8 Which was the only planet in the solar system not yet visited by a spacecraft as the 1990s began?

9 Who was developing *Hermes?*

10 And what was it?

11 What had Sergey Krikalev spent 313 days doing (1991-92)?

12 What major political change had he missed?

13 What kind of vehicle was the Ford *Explorer?*

14 By what abbreviation was the human immunodeficiency virus better known?

15 What Japanese creatures' breeding grounds were discovered after 60 years of marine investigation?

ANSWERS

1, Watching TV 2, Wolves (they were reintroduced) 3, Sir George Eyston's 1937 Thunderbolt 4, Kentish dormice 5, Silicone gel breast implants 6, Radioactive waste 7, Seville, Spain 8, Pluto 9, The European Space Agency 10, A manned shuttle 11, Orbiting the Earth 12, While he was away, his country, the Soviet Union, had ceased to exist 13, An off-road vehicle 14, HIV 15, Japanese eels

QUIZ 261

POT LUCK

1 What did Walter Diemer (died 1998) invent?

2 What was the 'cama', bred in Dubai?

3 What shone no more around Britain's coast after 1998?

4 Whose children were Nicholas, Kathryn and Euan?

5 Who were the first women twins elected to Parliament?

6 Which duo recorded *Kinky Boots* (1990)?

7 Which country's capital is Moroni?

8 Which country sold its old *Mirages* to Pakistan in 1990?

9 What were the *Mirages?*

10 And which other country got annoyed as a result?

11 Which Saudi owner saw his *Quest For Fame* win the Derby in 1990?

12 What nationality was soccer star Mario Kempes?

13 Which soccer team set a lowest-yet points total for the Premier League in 1994-95?

14 Which film actor played John Dunbar living among the Sioux?

15 And what was the film title?

ANSWERS

1, Bubble gum 2, Half camel, half llama 3, Manned lighthouses 4, Tony and Cherie Blair's 5, Angela and Maria Eagle 6, Patrick MacNee and Honor Blackman 7, Comoros 8, Australia 9, Jet planes 10, India 11, Khalid Abdullah 12, Argentine 13, Ipswich Town 14, Kevin Costner 15, *Dancing With Wolves*

QUIZ 262

TO WHICH COUNTRY DID THESE 90S SOCCER CLUBS BELONG?

1 Sturm Graz
2 Sparta Prague
3 Brondby
4 Olympiakos
5 Galatasaray
6 Bayern Munich
7 River Plate
8 Dynamo Minsk
9 Lazio
10 Barcelona
11 Dynamo Kiev
12 Barry Town
13 Cork City
14 Lens
15 Porto

ANSWERS

1, Austria 2, Czech Republic 3, Denmark 4, Greece 5, Turkey 6, Germany 7, Argentina 8, Belarus 9, Italy 10, Spain 11, Ukraine 12, Wales 13, Ireland 14, France 15, Portugal

MILITARY HARDWARE

1 What was Silkworms?
2 What kind of plane was the US F-117?
3 Which navy used the Sea Dart?
4 And what was it?
5 Which navy used Xia-class submarines?
6 What was the Abrams, used by the USA?
7 Which country made the Kfir?
8 And what was it?
9 Which country had an aircraft carrier named Foch?
10 What was the German Leopard?
11 What was the Nimrod used for?
12 Which country had the world's biggest submarines?
13 What was the US Air Force's B-1B?
14 And which 1950s design was still in service in a similar role?
15 Which veteran ships of the Iowa class were put back into 'mothballs' by the US Navy?

ANSWERS

1, Chinese missiles used by Iraq 2, The Stealth fighter 3, The British 4, An anti-missile missile 5, China's 6, A tank 7, Israel 8, A warplane 9, France 10, A tank 11, Maritime reconnaissance 12, Russia (Typhoon-class) 13, Its new strategic bomber 14, The B-52 15, Four WW2-vintage battleships

QUIZ 264

SPORT

SOCCER

1 From whom did Everton sign Gary Speed in 1996?

2 To which Magpies did he go on to play for?

3 Who joined Blackburn from Derby in 1998 for £5.3million?

4 In 1994 what did Mark Smith do in 19 seconds playing for Crewe?

5 Which striker scored 5 times for Man Utd v Ipswich in 1995?

6 Who beat Scotland in their first match of World Cup 90?

7 How many games did Scotland draw in the World Cup 98 finals?

8 Who was Scotland's manager in the 98 World Cup?

9 Which Welsh striker later took over the managing of Wales?

10 Which Welsh striker had an off-and-on relationship as coach with Real Madrid?

11 Which Arsenal star refused to fly?

12 And in which 1997 TV competition did he finish 1st, 2nd and 3rd?

13 Which Argentine managed Spurs in 93-94?

14 And who was his chairman?

15 Which keeper retired in 1997 after 1005 League appearances?

ANSWERS

1, Leeds United 2, Newcastle United 3, Christian Dailly 4, Get sent off 5, Andy Cole 6, Costa Rica 1-0 7, One, against Norway 8, Craig Brown 9, Mark Hughes 10, John Toshack 11, Dennis Bergkamp 12, Match of the Day's 'goal of the month' 13, Osvaldo Ardiles 14, Alan Sugar 15, Peter Shilton

QUIZ 265

POT LUCK

1 Which US animated TV show was a hit with kids despite (or because of) the swearing?

2 In which TV series did Sun Hill feature?

3 Complete this actress's name: Cloris-------?

4 In which sport did Michelle Smith become controversial?

5 What was Hyakutake?

6 For what was the Orange Prize awarded?

7 Which voyage features in the book *Every Man For Himself?*

8 Author?

9 Who was Aleksey II?

10 Which comic actor played Inspector Fowler in *The Thin Blue Line?*

11 Who put half a cow in formalin for art's sake?

12 In what sport did Cuba beat Japan to win a 1996 gold medal?

13 Wasps, Saracens, Harlequins were all successful – what?

14 On what subject did Jack Tinker write?

15 And which London theatre reopened with *Jesus Christ Superstar?*

ANSWERS

1, *South Park* 2, *The Bill* 3, Leachman 4, Swimming 5, A comet 6, A novel by a woman writer 7, The *Titanic's* 8, Beryl Bainbridge 9, Eastern Orthodox Patriarch of Russia 10, Rowan Atkinson 11, Damien Hirst 12, Baseball 13, English Rugby Union clubs 14, He was drama critic of the *Daily Mail* 15, The Lyceum

QUIZ 266

POT LUCK

1 What was 'Superman The Escape'?
2 Which US theme park opened its newest vertical drop ride in 1998?
3 What was its name?
4 Where was the 'Body Zone' being built in 1999?
5 Which London borough proclaimed itself The Millennium Borough?
6 Who married Ffion?
7 Which former Tory minister became a soccer pundit on radio?
8 Which London club's shirt had he been known to wear?
9 Who recorded *I'll Be Missing You* (1997)?
10 From which northern city did Chumbawamba hail?
11 What game did Woodforde and Woodbridge play better than most?
12 Who was Gordon Brown's wife?
13 Which soccer club did the Toon Army follow?
14 And who for a time was their favourite Frenchman?
15 In which TV show did Daisy and Onslow appear?

ANSWERS

1, The world's fastest rollercoaster 2, Alton Towers 3, Oblivion 4, The Millennium Dome 5, Greenwich 6, William Hague 7, David Mellor 8, Chelsea 9, Puff Daddy and Faith Evans 10, Leeds 11, Tennis (doubles) 12, He was unmarried at the end of the 90s 13, Newcastle United 14, David Ginola 15, *Keeping Up Appearances*

QUIZ 267

TRY THESE: CAPITALS OF COUNTRIES - 1999 VINTAGE.

1 Moldova
2 Mongolia
3 Nigeria
4 Dominica
5 Djibouti
6 Azerbaijan
7 Germany
8 The Gambia
9 Jordan
10 Latvia
11 Croatia
12 Czech Republic
13 Macedonia
14 Russia
15 Slovakia

ANSWERS

1, Chisinau 2, Ulan Bator 3, Abuja 4, Roseau 5, Djibouti 6, Baku 7, Berlin
8, Banjul 9, Amman 10, Riga 11, Zagreb 12, Prague 13, Skopje
14, Moscow 15, Bratislava

QUIZ 268

SCIENCE & TECHNOLOGY

1 The world's oldest person died in 1997: how old was she?

2 Where did she die?

3 Which space probe went to Europa?

4 And where was Europa?

5 Where were unusually old stone tools found in 1997: a) Siberia b) Sahara c) Mexico?

6 Prehistoric objects were also found in a German coal mine: what were they?

7 Whose 1718 pirate ship was discovered beneath the waves?

8 Which innovation did the Queen inaugurate with a message to students in Canada (1997)?

9 Who was 'Cheddar Man'?

10 And what fascinating link was proved between him and a local teacher?

11 Which ex-president made a parachute jump at the age of 72?

12 What was Hale-Bopp?

13 Which *Thunderbird* came to the end of the line?

14 For what eye condition was the major gene identified?

15 Which spacecraft shut down 10 billion km away from Earth?

ANSWERS

1, France 2, 122 3, *Galileo* 4, A moon of Jupiter 5, a) 6, Wooden spears 7, Blackbeard (Edward Teach) 8, The Royal Website 9, A 9000-year-old skeleton found in Somerset 10, DNA analysis established a genetic link between them 11, George Bush 12, A comet seen in 1997 13, Ford's car of that name 14, Congenital glaucoma 15, *Pioneer 10*

QUIZ 269

POT LUCK

1 Where did all 20 members of the Commission resign?

2 Who had been its president?

3 And who took over in his place?

4 Which was the first Harry Potter book: title please?

5 In which film did Eddie Murphy talk to animals?

6 For which British soccer club was Dennis Wise sometimes the only British player?

7 Who released an album called 'Come On Over'?

8 For which English county did cricketer Wasim Akram play?

9 Who co-ran a public relations firm called R J H?

10 What nationality was painter Arthur Boyd?

11 'Wilt the Stilt' died in 1999: who was he?

12 What game did Neil Back play?

13 Which US astronaut and moon-walker died in a motorcycle accident in 1999?

14 Which outspoken Tory came back to the Commons in 1997 but died in 1999?

15 Which 1993 publication from his pen had become a sensational bestseller?

ANSWERS

1, The European Union 2, Jacques Santer 3, Romano Prodi 4, Harry Potter
and the Philosopher's Stone 5, Dr Doolittle 6, Chelsea 7, Shania Twain
8, Lancashire 9, Sophie Rhys-Jones 10, Australian 11, US basketball star
Wilt Chamberlain 12, Rugby 13, Charles (Pete) Conrad 14, Alan Clark
15, His Diaries

QUIZ 270

WORLD EVENTS

1999

1 Which former Tanzanian leader died in 1999?

2 Which Caribbean state hanged nine convicts in four days?

3 Where was Kaynasli the scene of an earthquake?

4 Where did the Kabaka get married?

5 Where was Leonid Kuchma president?

6 Where did 750 lords lose their voting rights?

7 Where was the new territory of Nunavut?

8 Which European country's population was swollen by 15% by refugees?

9 Where were the refugees from?

10 Where did Ahmad Shah Masoud lead opposition troops?

11 Where was Bouteflika elected president?

12 Which state's capital was Praia?

13 Which country's population topped 1.3 billion?

14 And which country was close behind?

15 What was Zaire's new name?

ANSWERS

1, Julius Nyerere 2, Trinidad and Tobago 3, Turkey 4, Uganda 5, Ukraine 6, The UK (House of Lords reform) 7, Canada 8, Albania's 9, Kosovo 10, Afghanistan 11, Algeria 12, Cape Verde 13, China's 14, India 15, Democratic Republic of the Congo

QUIZ 271

PEOPLE

THEY ALL DIED IN 1995

1 He wrote *A Man For All Seasons*

2 Created E L Wisty

3 Mother of JFK

4 Champion of the 'little black dress'

5 Danced with Fred

6 Actor once married to Maggie Smith

7 Poet, once a Marxist, later knighted

8 Irish nuclear physicist

9 1940s 'sweater girl'

10 Prime Minister of India from 1977-79

11 Co-inventor of ENIAC, the first computer

12 Bernie the jet-setter and party-giver

13 Reggie's brother

14 Singing sister of Patty and LaVerne

15 Wartime voice of the BBC, from Canada

ANSWERS

1, Robert Bolt 2, Peter Cook 3, Rose Kennedy 4, Jean Muir 5, Ginger Rogers 6, Robert Stephens 7, Sir Stephen Spender 8, Ernest Walton 9, Lana Turner 10, Morarji Desai 11, J Presper Eckert 12, Bernard Cornfeld 13, Ronnie Kray 14, Maxene, of the Andrews Sisters 15, Stewart MacPherson

QUIZ 272

POT LUCK

1 To which politician was Jill Craigie married?

2 By what name did Ernest Wiseman (d. 1999) become famous?

3 Which ex-*Doctor in the House* was knighted in 1992?

4 For what controversial change did the Church of England vote in 1992?

5 With what organisation did Lord Killanin (d 1999) serve until 1980?

6 Where did Joshva Nkomo become vice president in 1990?

7 Where did Oliver Reed die in 1999?

8 Which actor won a 1997 Emmy for *12 Angry Men?*

9 Which magazine did Liz Tilberis edit from 1992?

10 Which singer, who died in 1999, was born Frank Abelson in Liverpool?

11 And what was his signature song?

12 Who wrote *Vanishing Point* (1996)?

13 What role did Liz Dawn play in *Coronation Street?*

14 What was David Black's best athletics event?

15 For which Premiership club did Nigel Martyn keep goal?

ANSWERS

1, Michael Foot 2, Ernie Wise 3, Dirk Bogarde 4, Ordination of women 5, International Olympic Committee president 6, Zimbabwe 7, Malta 8, George C Scott 9, *Harper's Bazaar* 10, Frankie Vaughan 11, *Give Me The Moonlight* 12, Morris West 13, Vera Duckworth 14, 400 metres 15, Leeds United

QUIZ 273

SCIENCE & TECHNOLOGY

1 How did a star disrupt communications in 1998?

2 What were AOL and Demon offering people?

3 Computer buffs beware: what did US psychologists warn damages 'personal well being'?

4 Where was a Phoenician ship seen again?

5 And what kind of machine saw it?

6 What atmospheric phenomenon observed in 1998 was 5% bigger than in 1996?

7 What unusual fish was caught off Indonesia?

8 Where had these fish previously been found?

9 Whose Space Agency was running out of cash?

10 And who agreed to buy 'space-time' for its astronauts from the ailing organization?

11 Which Nobel Prize did Amartya Sen win in 1998?

12 What was HDTV?

13 Where was the most famous 'Silicon Valley'?

14 What was Leonid, seen in November 1998?

15 Where was sewage from McMurdo Station causing problems?

ANSWERS

1, A blast of cosmic radiation struck the Earth from a 'star-flare'? 2, Internet access. 3, Home use of the Internet 4, In the Mediterranean 5, A robot submersible 6, The ozone hole over the Antarctic 7, Two coelacanths 8, Off southern Africa 9, Russia's 10, NASA 11, Economics 12, Digital high definition television 13, California 14, A meteor storm 15, Antarctica (almost 1000 people were based there)

QUIZ 274

SPORT

SOCCER

1 Who sold Paul Merson to Middlesbrough in 1997?

2 And from whom did they sign Dennis Bergkamp in 1995?

3 How much was the Bergkamp transfer fee: a)£3m b)£5m or c)£7.5m?

4 Which Italian striker moved from Juventus to Milan in 1995?

5 Which club sold him to Juventus in 1990 for a then-record fee?

6 Which famous coach, notably for Inter Milan, died in November 1997?

7 Which two old rivals met in the Delle Alpe, Turin on 4 July 1990?

8 What controversial method decided the game after extra time?

9 Which Russian goalkeeper, holder of 78 caps, died in 1990?

10 For which country did Zico play before retiring in 1992?

11 Which English club won the championship in 1993 after a 25-year gap?

12 Who was the club captain, though injured most of the season?

13 Which club did he move to as player-coach in 1994?

14 For which country did Frank Rijkaard play and later coach?

15 Who managed France to the 1992 European Championships?

ANSWERS

1, Arsenal 2, Inter Milan 3, c) 4, Roberto Baggio 5, Fiorentina 6, Helenio Herrera 7, West Germany and England 8, A penalty shoot-out 9, Lev Yashin 10, Brazil 11, Manchester United 12, Bryan Robson 13, Middlesbrough 14, Holland 15, Michel Platini

QUIZ 275

POT LUCK

1 Which US actor led the search for 'Private Ryan'?

2 Which comedian directed the film *Bullets Over Broadway* but didn't appear in it?

3 Which woman actors co-starred in *Thelma and Louise?*

4 In which film series did Jesse make friends?

5 What kind of animal was *Babe?*

6 And what did Babe think it was?

7 In which war was the TV drama *Bravo Two Zero* set?

8 Who became BBC director-general in 1993?

9 In which musical did Patti Lupone play Norma Desmond?

10 Who wrote the show's music?

11 Who wrote a play called *Time Of My Life?*

12 Who released a solo album called 'Wandering Spiri't at the age of 50?

13 Where was Milan Kucan president?

14 Which soccer club did Paul Bracewell manage (1999)?

15 And who led a 'second October Revolution' in Russia (lasting one day)?

ANSWERS

1, Tom Hanks 2, Woody Allen 3, Susan Sarandon and Geena Davis
4, The *Free Willy* movies 5, A pig 6, A sheep 7, The Gulf War 8, John Birt
9, *Sunset Boulevard* 10, Andrew Lloyd Webber 11, Alan Ayckbourne
12, Mick Jagger 13, Slovenia 14, Fulham 15, Boris Yeltsin in 1993

QUIZ 276

NAME THE COUNTRIES YOU ASSOCIATE WITH THESE PEOPLE.

1 Daw Aung Suu Kyi
2 Bob Dole
3 Sani Abacha
4 Suharto
5 Eduard Shevardnadze
6 Paul Keating
7 Haris Slajdzic
8 Boris Yeltsin
9 Wei Jingsheng
10 Fidel Castro
11 Fidel Ramos
12 Hastings Banda
13 Archbishop Desmond Connell
14 Queen Margrethe II
15 Hojatolislam Rafsanjani

ANSWERS

1. Myanmar (Burma) 2. United States 3. Nigeria 4. Indonesia 5. Georgia
6. Australia 7. Bosnia 8. Russia 9. China 10. Cuba 11. Philippines
12. Malawi 13. Ireland 14. Denmark 15. Iran

QUIZ 277

SCIENCE & TECHNOLOGY

1 Which vintage spacecraft was raised from a watery grave in 1999?

2 What had happened to it?

3 Which nation seemed to be next in line to put people into space as the decade ended?

4 Which spacecraft suggested this with a 21-hour flight?

5 What happened to the Mars Climate Orbiter?

6 What error was blamed?

7 Did the Mars Polar Lander make up for this?

8 What was 9969 Braille?

9 After whom was the *Chandra* X ray satellite named?

10 What did Sea Launch plan to use as a rocket base?

11 Which Soviet space station was shut down in 1999?

12 What was Upsilon Andromedae?

13 And why was it exciting?

14 Which spacecraft sent back pictures of Ganymede and Io?

15 And around which planet did these bodies move?

ANSWERS

1, The US Mercury capsule *Liberty Bell 7* 2, It sank after splashdown in 1961 3, China 4, It launched the *Shenzhou* craft and brought it back to Earth 5, It burned up 6, Incorrect conversion from English to metric units by engineers 7, No, it vanished without trace 8, An asteroid 9, Astrophysicist Subrahmanyan Chandrasekhar 10, A mobile oil platform 11, Mir 12, A star 13, It had three planets orbiting it 14, *Galileo* 15, Jupiter

QUIZ 278

POT LUCK

1 To which political party did Malcolm Bruce belong?

2 Of which football club was Karren Brady the chief executive?

3 Which radio programme did John Humphries co-present?

4 Were the characters in the film *Backdraft* a) fireman b) bankers c) double glazing salesmen?

5 What happened to US singer Selena in 1995?

6 Which Broadway show won Chita Rivera a Tony award?

7 Which tennis star set a 1993 record with 1011 aces?

8 Who was the founder of The Body Shop?

9 Which purple dinosaur was a hit with children?

10 By what name was musician Dave Evans better known?

11 And with what band did he achieve success?

12 Which country's king was crowned for the second time in 1993?

13 Who became the fastest-selling fiction writer of modern times?

14 Which castle was damaged by fire in 1992?

15 And which building was opened to visitors to help pay for repairs?

ANSWERS

1, Liberal Democrats 2, Birmingham City 3, *Today* (BBC4) 4, a) 5, She was murdered 6, *Kiss of the Spider Woman* 7, Pete Sampras 8, Anita Roddick 9, Barney 10, The Edge 11, U2 12, Cambodia's Norodom Sihanouk 13, John Grisham 14, Windsor Castle 15, Buckingham Palace

QUIZ 279

SCIENCE & TECHNOLOGY

1 Which natural process did genetics scientists claim to be close to slowing down?

2 Which spacecraft launched in 1977 was still functioning in deep space?

3 What record did it establish in February 1998?

4 What, according to a US scientist, might hit the earth in 2028?

5 And which body said within 24 hours 'oh no it won't'?

6 In which continent was the Trans-Kalahari Railway completed?

7 What kind of mail did Cyber Promotions Inc. send?

8 Which South African wildlife reserve was 100 years old in 1998?

9 What proportion of planet species were said to be at risk of extinction: a) 20% b) 12.5% c) 5%?

10 Was I M Pei famous as a nuclear physicist, a heart surgeon or an architect?

11 What nationality is he?

12 Which controversial piece of cloth went on public show in 1998?

13 Which country agreed to set aside 10% of its rainforest for conservation?

14 In which European country did mine waste threaten a natural reserve?

15 And can you name the reserve?

ANSWERS

1, The ageing process 2, *Voyager 1* 3, It was the furthest man-made object from Earth 4, An asteroid 5, NASA 6, Africa 7, Junk e-mail 8, Kruger National Park 9, b) 10, An architect 11, American 12, The Shroud of Turin 13, Brazil 14, Spain 15, The Coto Donana

QUIZ 280

WORLD EVENTS

THE YEAR WAS 1995

1 What devastated Kobe?

2 And in what country is Kobe?

3 Which country had a minister for Francophone Affairs?

4 With whom did Peru fight a three-week war?

5 For what crime was Timothy McVeigh arrested?

6 Where were thousands of Hutu people massacred?

7 Which wartime event was remembered 50 years on?

8 What day did most nations mark this event?

9 Which of the wartime Allies was a day late?

10 Which wartime leader's papers were bought by the British government?

11 Which European country was troubled by a paedophile scandal?

12 What disease reached epidemic proportions in Zaire?

13 Where was Mubarak shot at?

14 Who was he?

15 And why was he where he was?

ANSWERS

1, An earthquake 2, Japan 3, France 4, Ecuador 5, The Oklahoma City bombing in the USA 6, Rwanda 7, VE Day 8, May 8 9, Russia 10, Churchill 11, Belgium 12, Ebola fever 13, Addis Ababa, Ethiopia 14, President of Egypt 15, He was attending a OAU summit

QUIZ 281

SPORT

SOCCER

1 For which London club did Gordon Durie play in season 1991-92?

2 Which cup became the Rumbelows Cup for 1991-92?

3 Who sponsored it for the 1993 season?

4 Which club was expelled from the Football League in 1992?

5 Which Scottish club boasted three international goalkeepers in 1991?

6 Can you name them?

7 In which country was Serie A the premier league?

8 Who scored for Liverpool in their 1981 European Cup final win?

9 Whom did Liverpool beat?

10 Which Spanish club won its first-ever European Cup in 1992?

11 And where did they win it?

12 The previous year they'd lost a European final: to which British club?

13 Which Italian club had 17 internationals at the start of the 92-93 season?

14 Three were Dutch: can you name them?

15 For whom did Jean-Pierre Papin play international soccer?

ANSWERS

1, Tottenham Hotspur 2, The Littlewoods Cup 3, Coca-Cola 4, Aldershot
5, Rangers 6, Andy Goram (Scotland), Chris Woods (England), Bonni
Ginzburg(Israel) 7, Italy 8, Alan Kennedy 9, Real Madrid 10, Barcelona
11, Wembley, beating Sampdoria 1-0 12, Man Utd beat them in the
Cupwinner's Cup Final 13, AC Milan 14, Ruud Gullit, Marco Van Basten,
Frank Rijkaard

QUIZ 282

POT LUCK

1 Which country's parliament was the Eduskunta?
2 Who was Russia's 'golden girl' of tennis?
3 Which rugby league team acquired the name Wild Cats?
4 Which member of the Kennedy family died in a 1999 plane crash?
5 In which city was the Earth's 'official' 6-billionth person born?
6 Which actress was married to Liam Neeson?
7 Which musical-composer's real name was Lionel Begleiter (he died in 1999)?
8 Where did the world's largest dome open on 31 December 1999?
9 What were minkes, being chased by Japanese?
10 Hsing-Hsing died in 1999: who or what was he/she?
11 What did Anne-Sophie Mutter do better than most?
12 In which bestseller did Muggles feature?
13 And what were Muggles?
14 What was Linux?
15 In which country was Shania Twain born?

ANSWERS

1, Iceland 2, Anna Kournikova 3, Wakefield Trinity 4, John F Kennedy Jr 5, Sarayevo 6, Natasha Richardson 7, Lionel Bart 8, Greenwich 9, Whales 10, Washington Zoo's giant panda (male) 11, Play the violin 12, The Harry Potter books 13, Non-magicians 14, A computer operating system 15, Canada

QUIZ 283

ARTS & ENTERTAINMENT

1 In which TV show did John Thaw play a barrister?

2 Which actress played 'Hyacinth Bucket'?

3 Name the show in which she starred?

4 Was her screen husband's name Richard, John or Henry?

5 And can you name the actor who played him?

6 What organization featured in *The Knock?*

7 And which actress played agent Katherine Roberts in this series before going on to bigger things?

8 Which actress was 'Dr Quin'?

9 And what was the full title of her TV series?

10 Which soap went thrice-weekly in Britain from 1994?

11 Who played Kathy Beale (Mitchell) in it?

12 In which TV series did Dr Beth Glover appear?

13 And who played her?

14 Name the female detective in *Prime Suspect.*

15 And the actress who played the role.

ANSWERS

1, *Kavanagh QC* 2, Patricia Routledge 3, *Keeping Up Appearances* 4, Richard 5, Clive Swift 6, HM Customs and Excise 7, Alex Kingston 8, Jane Seymour 9, *Dr Quin: Medicine Woman* 10, *EastEnders* 11, Gillian Taylforth 12, *Peak Practice* 13, Amanda Burton 14, Jane Tennison 15, Helen Mirren

QUIZ 284

SCIENCE & TECHNOLOGY

1 Which computer giant faced an anti-trust lawsuit in the USA?

2 What universal modem system was adopted by the ITU in 1998?

3 What did the initials ATS mean to camera buffs?

4 Which new toy responded when tickled?

5 What subject was discussed at an international conference at Kyoto in 1997?

6 Which of these had doubled since 1960: a) freshwater use b) carbon dioxide emissions c) fish stocks?

7 What was the 'Erasmus' programme?

8 By what name was the drug sildenafil better known?

9 Which great apes faced new dangers from forest fires?

10 What was *Lunar Prospector?*

11 Which planet's rings were found to be made of red soot-like dust?

12 What do the initials ESA stand for?

13 What kind of vehicle was the prototype X-33?

14 What was Alvin being used for?

15 What creature was found living at a temperature of 80°C?

ANSWERS

1, Microsoft 2, 56,000 bits-per-second, or 56k 3, Advanced Photo System 4, The Furby 5, Climate Change 6, a) and b) 7, An exchange-student scheme in the EU 8, Viagra 9, Orang-utans in Indonesia 10, A spacecraft sent to orbit the Moon (1998) 11, Jupiter's 12, European Space Agency 13, A new Space Shuttle 14, Deep-sea research 15, A deep sea worm (the most heat-resistant organism so far discovered)

QUIZ 285

POT LUCK

1 Whose company was Lucasfilm?

2 Where were Falung Gong exercises practised?

3 From which country did Ladysmith Black Mambazo come?

4 What did they do?

5 Who agreed to join the London Philharmonic as principal conductor from 2000?

6 Was Tony Lockett a) cricketer b) Australian Rules footballer or c) tennis player?

7 Where did Muhammad VI become king in 1999?

8 Where was Britain's 1999 royal wedding of the year?

9 And who were the happy couple?

10 Of which Latin American band was Ricky Martin a former member?

11 Were Dinos and Jake Chapman a) artists b) singers c) footballers?

12 Who was Belize's permanent representative at the UN?

13 And how did he make news in 1999?

14 Whose extradition did Judge Balthasar Garzon seek?

15 Did Jan Ullrich ride bikes, drive cars or hit tennis balls?

ANSWERS

1, George Lucas 2, China 3, South Africa 4, Sing 5, Kurt Masur 6, a) 7, Morocco 8, Windsor Castle 9, Prince Edward and Sophie Rhys-Jones 10, Menudo 11, a) 12, Michael Ashcroft 13, He became Conservative Party treasurer 14, General Pinochet's 15, He was a cyclist

QUIZ 286

SPORT

1997

1 Who was Jon Bigg's retiring wife?

2 Who was world snooker champion?

3 Which Scot coached the British Lions?

4 What did Tony Dobbin do?

5 Who said 'I'm a Cablinasian'?

6 Who said 'Boxers should eat before they fight'?

7 And of whom?

8 Who said it wasn't nice being spoken of as 'a dodgy keeper'?

9 Which soccer coach said 'They make from a little mosquito a big elephant'?

10 Of whom was he speaking?

11 Which London club sacked Bruce Rioch as its manager?

12 What nationality was David Ginola?

13 And which London side did he move to from Newcastle United?

14 Which cricketer scored 63 for England on his first visit to Lord's?

15 Which Welshman played cricket for England?

ANSWERS

1, Sally Gunnell 2, Ken Doherty 3, Ian McGeechan 4, Raise horses: an Irish jockey 5, Tiger Woods (on his roots) 6, Sylvester Stallone 7, Mike Tyson 8, David James 9, Ruud Gullit 10, The British media 11, QPR 12, French 13, Tottenham Hotspur 14, Ben Hollioake 15, Robert Croft

QUIZ 287

POT LUCK

1 Who owned the Skywalker Ranch film studios?

2 What title did Edward Anthony Richard Louis Windsor acquire in 1999?

3 What sport did Don King promote?

4 Which actress played Elizabeth Bennett on TV in a Jane Austen classic?

5 And which Austen book was dramatised?

6 Ben Affleck and Rupert Graves were both a) actors b) footballers c) pop stars?

7 What was pop singer Billie's surname?

8 What nationality was Cate Blanchett?

9 What art prize did Steve McQueen win?

10 Who became Britain's first woman sports minister?

11 Who was chairman of the 'decommissioning body' in Northern Ireland?

12 And what were to be decommissioned?

13 What British sporting prize did Lindsay Davenport win in 1999?

14 In what political party was Steve Norris prominent?

15 Miucca Prada and Matteo Thun were both a) Mafia bosses b) fashion designers c) Chelsea footballers?

ANSWERS

1, George Lucas 2, Earl of Wessex 3, Boxing 4, Jennifer Ehle 5, *Pride and Prejudice* 6, a) 7, Piper 8, Australian 9, The Turner Prize 10, Kate Hoey 11, General John de Chastelain 12, Weapons 13 The Wimbledon ladies championship 14, Conservative Party 15, b)

QUIZ 288

POT LUCK

1 In which TV series did Data the encyclopedia android appear?

2 In which TV series did Victoria Wood appear as 'Bren'?

3 Thomas Terry Hoar Stevens died in 1990: what was his stage name?

4 Who presented *You Bet* from 1991?

5 *You Rang M'Lord* starred Paul Shane: in which earlier holiday camp series had he appeared?

6 Which game show was hosted by Richard O'Brien?

7 What was Inspector Morse's first name?

8 And what was Sergeant Lewis's?

9 In what TV show was 'Ken Melvin' killed by a bomb in 1990?

10 In which TV show did 'Dr Grayling Russell' appear as a character?

11 Who played Judith Fitzgerald in *Cracker?*

12 Which Doctor did Paul McGann play in 1996?

13 Who played Gaz in *The Full Monty?*

14 Which Greek character was 'Disneyfied'?

15 What disaster struck the Earth in the film *Deep Impact?*

ANSWERS

1, *Star Trek: The Next Generation* 2, *Dinner Ladies* 3, Terry-Thomas 4, Matthew Kelly 5, *Hi-de-Hi* 6, *The Crystal Maze* 7, Endeavour 8, Robbie 9, *The Bill* 10, *Inspector Morse* 11, Barbara Flynn 12, Dr Who 13, Robert Carlyle 14, Hercules 15, A comet

QUIZ 289

WORLD EVENTS

1993

1 Which Central American civil war ended?

2 Where did Moi face opposition?

3 Where did seven US Jews visit a country normally closed to Jewish visitors?

4 Which Irish leader decided it was time to go?

5 Which 'war' was now history, according to President Bush?

6 Where was Fumio Abe accused of bribery?

7 What was the Party of God in Arabic?

8 Which Commonwealth country planned to limit immigration?

9 Where was Rodney King beaten by police?

10 Where were political foes told to kneel before their king?

11 Which country tested its biggest nuclear device?

12 Why did the US Secretary of the Navy resign?

13 Where did the UN host a conference on the environment?

14 Where did Yitzhak Shamir lose an election?

15 Which former East German leader was extradited from Moscow to stand trial in Germany?

ANSWERS

1, El Salvador 2, Kenya 3, Saudi Arabia 4, Charles Haughey 5, The Cold War 6, Japan 7, Hezbollah 8, Australia 9, Los Angeles, USA 10, Thailand 11, China 12, Women had accused male officers of harassment 13, Rio de Janeiro 14, Israel 15, Erich Honecker

QUIZ 290

SPORT

1 Who was Ayrton Senna's team mate for McLaren in 1990?

2 Who won the 1990 US Masters golf title?

3 Where were the 1994 Winter Olympic Games held?

4 Spurs lost against Chelsea 3-2 on 1 December 1990 and were fined for being late. Why?

5 Which Argentinian did David Beckham 'kick out' at in St Etienne during the 1998 World Cup?

6 How many seconds did it take Vinny Jones to be booked in his match on 19 January 1991?

7 How many press-ups did Charles Servizio complete during 24 hours in California, April 1993?

8 Name the first male British gymnast to win a medal at the World Championships in 1993.

9 In a 1990 Gallup Poll, which famous racehorse achieved higher public recognition than Norman Lamont, the Chancellor?

10 Which Rugby League player broke the transfer record in 1992 when transferring from Widnes to Wigan for £440,000?

11 Why did Doncaster Rovers' goalkeeper, Ken Hardwick, not get to play in the England Under 23's trial in January 1995 after being asked to?

12 In 1990, at Victoria, Australian cricketer Gary Chapman scored a record number of runs from one ball with no overthrows. What was his score?

13 Who scored the last goal for France in the 1998 football World Cup Final?

14 Which three football teams were promoted to the Premiership in 1997 only to be relegated the following year?

15 Which Italian footballer missed the deciding penalty to give Brazil victory in the 1994 World Cup Finals?

ANSWERS

1, Gerhard Berger 2, Nick Faldo 3, Lillehammer, Norway 4, Team coach was towed away 5, Diego Simone 6, Five 7, 46,001 8, Neil Thomas 9, Desert Orchid 10, Martin Offiah 11, He was 30 years old! 12, 17 13, Emmanuel Petit 14, Barnsley, Bolton and Crystal Palace 15, Roberto Baggio

QUIZ 291

POP MUSIC

1 Who won best the Best Male Artist Award in the 1998 BRITs?

2 Who were 'Walking on Sunshine', when they won the 1997 Eurovision Song Contest with, 'Love Shine a Light'?

3 Who, in 1998, performed the 'Ballad of Tom Jones'?

4 All Saints had their first hit in March 1998. What was the song?

5 Which British band were on 'Hope Street' in 1995?

6 In 1997, the four piece band Aqua topped the charts with 'The Barbie Song'. What nationality are they?

7 In 1998 which two bands held a concert in Belfast to support the, 'Yes', campaign for the referendum on the Good Friday Agreement?

8 Which band recorded, 'Three Lions', with David Baddiel and Frank Skinner for Euro '96 and the 1998 World Cup?

9 In 1998, which US teen band was made up of Taylor, Isaac and Zac?

10 In 1997 and 1998 who topped the Album charts with, 'Urban Hymns'?

11 Vanessa Mae reached number 16 in Jan 1995 with 'Toccata and Fugue'. What instrument did she play?

12 In Sept 1996 the Cardigans reached number 21 with 'Lovefool'. From what album did the track come?

13 In September 1996, Mariah Carey reached number 3 with 'Endless Love'. Which male soul singer dueted with her on this track?

14 Which member of Take That left the band to pursue a solo career in July 1995?

15 In 1992, Whitney Houston reached number 1 with, 'I Will Always Love You'. From which movie does the song come?

ANSWERS

1, Finley Quaye 2, Katrina and the Waves 3, Space 4, 'Never Ever' 5, The Levellers 6, Danish 7, U2 & Ash 8, Lightning Seeds 9, Hanson 10, The Verve 11, Violin 12, First Band on the Moon 13, Luther Vandross 14, Robbie Williams 15, The Bodyguard

NOTES

NOTES

NOTES

NOTES

NOTES

NOTES

NOTES

NOTES

NOTES

NOTES

NOTES

NOTES

NOTES

NOTES

NOTES